DO YOU KNOW WHY THE CRITICS
AT A CONCERT ... NOT HEAR ... SAME N...

MEZZANINE

Date Due

D0559507

HE FUNDA... ...NO ...LY

THE LOCA... ...KES A
GREAT D... ...
IN THE M... ...
A VIOLIN ...

GRASSHOPPERS HAVE THEIR EARS
IN THEIR LEGS;
THEY ARE SENSI-
TIVE TO A WIDE
RANGE OF PITCH·

A FUGUE

IN CYCLES AND BELS

A FUGUE
IN CYCLES AND BELS

BY

JOHN MILLS

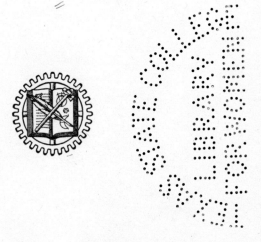

NEW YORK

D. VAN NOSTRAND COMPANY

250 FOURTH AVENUE

PREFACE

This book is written for those who may wish to know what science is doing to music and what it can do for music. Until the first quarter of this century, when the electron was discovered and put to work in the vacuum tube, music had developed with only small contributions from the physical sciences. The electrical arts of communication then supplied apparatus and techniques to increase enormously the size of musical audiences. Radio carries music to millions; improved methods of recording permit its preservation and reproduction long after the original sounds have ceased; and motion pictures are accompanied by music electrically reproduced.

These electrical developments have had great effects socially and economically, and also upon the profession of music. Upon the art, so far, they have not had much effect. Quietly, however, in their own technical advances they have been laying the basis for a revolutionary change in music itself.

This is a matter of possible concern to musicians and music lovers. The revolution, which is inevitable, may be forecast or guided only by those who know with some exactness what electricity can do. This book gives those facts with as little technicality as is possible, emphasizing not how the wheels go round but where they may take us. For the discussion two strange but con-

v

venient words are required, cycles and bels. These ideas, which are not difficult, are introduced in Part I.

The final test of music will always be the trained and critical ear. During the past twenty years there have been important researches on hearing with particular reference to the perception of musical tones. The results of these investigations are given in Part II. The human ear has such a delicate complexity of structure and response that this portion of the book is necessarily the most difficult. Fortunately its material is not all necessary for understanding the electrical future of music. Part II, therefore, may be skipped on the first reading; and it should be by readers who are primarily interested in what electricity can do for music.

Why electricity will influence composers and directors is told in Part III; how it can produce new tonal effects or enhance old; and how it permits artistic effects previously unattainable.

It is a pleasure to acknowledge the assistance of Dr. J. C. Steinberg, Member of the Technical Staff, Bell Telephone Laboratories, who read this book in manuscript and in proof.

J. M.

CONTENTS

CONTENTS

PART ONE

FROM PYTHAGORAS TO BELL

1 PURITY AND PITCH

Far back in human history, perhaps contemporaneous with the evolution in their present form of the ear and the vocal organs, are hidden the origins of music, the most instinctive of arts. The primordial man who first thrilled at the sound of his own voice or enhanced his emotions with the growl of fight, or chase, foreshadowed the fundamental appeal which music would increasingly exert as the ages passed.

The development of artistic sense may have started with the pleasurable repetition of meaningless sounds. It would seem possible that unconscious experimentation with the larynx and with the resonant chambers of the mouth developed howls which later became singing tones. When these rose, or fell, in certain ways they pleased most; certain musical intervals came to be accepted by ear; and there was the beginning of a scale.

At what stage in the evolution the sonorous effects of inanimate matter were first appreciated—when, for example, a hollow tree became a drum and instruments were formed—we may never know, for these events, like the origin of the simple tools of wheel and lever, are lost in the ages before recorded history.

In so far as the child repeats the history of the race some of the pleasure in the origin of music is discernible in the delight of the infant babbling in his crib or enjoying a repeated percussion of his bottle against its sides. Later he will discover the musical tone of a plucked string and the sound a pipe emits when he blows across its open end. But in these days of five-and-ten-cent toys he will not need to reinvent any of the primitive instruments. He is the heir to all the inventions of the ages; and his musical education, except as modified by his own genius, will be that of his time and place.

When he goes to high school, a few days of his course in physics, if he takes one, will be devoted to acoustics. With a sonometer, the modern laboratory form of a monochord, he may have a chance to repeat some experiments of Pythagoras. In that case he will tune two similar strings to the same pitch; and then alter one by a bridge to study the relation of lengths when the tones are consonant.

When one string is twice as long as the other, that is when the lengths are as two is to one—in the ratio of 2/1—the shorter gives the octave of the longer. The Greeks had a word for it: they made a practice of magadizing, singing in octaves and enjoying tones in unison. This numerical relation for the octave was one of the first discoveries of Pythagoras. He found also the ratio 3/2 for the interval known as a Fifth and 4/3 for the Fourth; but he failed to detect the major third, corresponding to the ratio 5/4, which did not enter into the music of his day. Instead, he discovered a pleasing interval in the ratio 81/64 which is so near to 5/4, that is to 80/64, as to be scarcely distinguishable when it occurs in ordinary music.

The final result of the Pythagorean investigation is summarized in the statement that the smaller the numbers which enter into the ratio, or, in other words, the simpler the ratio, the more perfect the consonance. A mathematical basis appeared to have been given to music; but was it so after all? Actually what had been accomplished was the first physical measurement of what the ear liked. Stripped of the mystical appeal of simple numbers, and the connotation of the music of the spheres to which the philosopher devoted much of his attention, the relations which he found were after the fact. Early man learned to like barbecued beef and the fermented juice of the grape: the later scientist discovered that these were animal proteins and ethyl alcohol. The human ear had certain preferences in the matter of succeeding or simultaneous tones; and Pythagoras weighed and measured them. He did not, however, discover any reason for the ratios which he determined.

When similar experiments are performed in high school the student is usually given some reasons; but if he were repeating the history of the race he would have to wait for a time at least comparable to the twenty-one centuries which followed Pythagoras before there was further progress in the scientific description of the phenomena of music.

In those intervening years music progressed as an art, establishing its scales, devising notations, and developing its theories of harmony. It evolved without benefit of physics, except in so far as the simple rules of Pythagoras gave support to certain musical intervals against possible changes in taste, or style, and provided a reproducible standard for their calibration.

The discoveries of Pythagoras, although they in-

volved experimentation, were on the whole typical of
the Greek philosophers. A century earlier Thales discovered magnetism in the case of the natural magnetic
ore which was to be found in those parts; but there was
no scientific investigation until the work of Gilbert, a
court physician of Queen Elizabeth. Democritus will
always be credited as the first exponent of atomic
theory; but there was no evidence upon which legiti-
mate inference could be based until Dalton's work in
the early nineteenth century. The Greeks were excellent geometricians and philosophers, but they were not
experimenters; they observed and speculated upon
what they saw, but rarely did they set up experiments
to check their a priori conclusions or to extend those
that could be verified.

The scientific method was practically unknown until
the sixteenth century. Of its scientists the most produc-
tive was Galileo. As a youth of twenty-five he deduced
the law relating the length of a pendulum to the time
required for its swing, carrying out his observation
upon the swinging lamps of the cathedral in Pisa and
using for a timepiece his own pulse. Although his major
contributions were to mechanics and astronomy he developed some techniques for acoustics and gave im-
petus to researches in that field.

He recognized that sound is due to vibrations of air
against the ear drum, although actual proof of the fact
that air is the medium awaited an experiment in 1705,
when an English scientist placed a clock in such a
vacuum as was then obtainable and showed that its tick
was no longer audible. Galileo studied the vibrations
of strings, as did Pythagoras, but he took into account

not only their lengths but also their thickness and the tension with which they were strung. With his experiments starts our modern knowledge of acoustics.

Galileo was followed a few years later by another investigator, so much less famous that he is frequently omitted in historical accounts. This was the Jesuit Mersenne, who was well informed as to Galileo's methods for he translated the latter's works and made them known in France. During the later years of his life Mersenne gave up the field of theological disquisition for that of acoustics and published his results in 1636 as "Harmonie Universelle."

Mersenne's experiments with strings illustrate the laboratory methods of his time and his own ingenuity. He stretched a cord about a hundred feet long, so long that he could easily follow its swings by eye and count their number in some unit of time. Then he shortened the cord successively to one-half, one-third, and one-quarter of its original length. He found the vibrations, respectively, two, three and four times as frequent, deriving thereby the relationship that, other things being equal, the vibration frequency of a string is inversely as its length. Then, knowing the law, he shortened the cord until it emitted a musical tone when its vibrations were too rapid to be observed. From the length he could compute the number of vibrations per second.

By adjusting the length of a vibrating string until its note was of the same pitch as some other source of sound, for example, an organ pipe, he was able to state the number of vibrations each second which that source established in the air; and so to define the pitch of a source in terms of its frequency.

"Frequency" was the word he used—or rather "frequentia," in the Latin of his original edition. Frequency is the number of times a second a cyclical effect occurs. When the current in an electric light oscillates, some sixty times a second, first flowing in one direction, then in the other, and again in the original direction there is a cyclic change just as there is in the vibration of a string or in the to-and-fro motion of a pendulum. In any case the number of times a second that a cycle repeats is the frequency of the particular effect.

As Mersenne definitely proved, pitch and frequency are directly related; and the pitch of a musical tone can be quantitatively described by the corresponding frequency in cycles per second. An important relationship for tones was thus established between a psychological characteristic and a physical quantity. The objective basis for the appraisal of the pitch of a sound is the vibration frequency of its source. Between the source and the brain, which perceives the pitch, there intervene the air, in which the vibrations are transmitted, and a mechanism, the ear, for the translation of air waves into a sensation which in turn gives rise to a perception. Pitch, however, is not a subjective judgment; but, on the other hand, it is not independent of what happens within the head of the auditor. Only in so far as the ear renders a faithful translation is there exact correspondence between pitch and frequency.

Translation is always subject to a charge of inexactness for some intrusion of the personality of a translator is usually possible. Mechanisms which perform similar functions, by transferring information from one medium to another, have their own peculiarities and are liable to distort when the conditions are exceptional. This is particularly true for all mechanisms which translate wave motion when one of the media is ponderable, as from air to electricity or vice versa. For any device of this character, and the human ear falls into this class, experimental analysis will reveal its limitations and will permit the accurate prediction of the distortion of which it will be guilty.

When the ear is considered as a translating device which may introduce distortions, the experimental results of Mersenne present a new aspect. The direct dependence which he found for frequency and pitch can be interpreted as evidence that the ear is a faithful translator of such musical sound as he utilized. Where Pythagoras determined what succession of sounds was pleasing, and so obtained an esthetic criterion for musical intervals, Mersenne made the first experimental analysis of the ear itself.

Similar results were obtained by all the investigators who followed him, as long as they utilized such natural sources of sound as the conventional musical instruments and the organs of speech. Within the limits, of type and intensity of sound, inherent in these sources the ear is a perfect translator of frequency into pitch. There were, it is true, some devices available, constructed on the principles of a siren, which could have produced very loud sounds and also could have been adapted to musical sounds fundamentally unlike those of ordinary instruments. Perhaps because the relationship of pitch and frequency was universally accepted and seemed so logical, these sirens were almost never used to extend the range of sounds over which the ear was tested; and its latent infidelity was not disclosed.

Sounds beyond the type of ordinary instruments were needed, sounds delicately contrived and accurately determined. These were not available until the electrical art of communication developed. For its own advancement on the side of telephony this new art required as complete and as accurate an investigation of hearing as was possible. In the attempt to obtain the desired data new principles were discovered, new apparatus invented, and new arts established. A by-product of the investigation was the discovery of conditions under which the pitch perceived does not have its usual correspondence to frequency. Under those conditions, in effect, pitch is subjective; a listener hears what physically does not exist in the air around his ears.

These developments and their bearing upon music will be described in later chapters. For the present the important point is the desirability of distinguishing between a sound and its perception. Sound must be described in terms of frequencies, in cycles per second, to which the pitch may, or may not, conform.

In their study of the frequency-pitch relationship, the investigators of the seventeenth century came upon a phenomenon which was necessary to the later explanation of the Pythagorean law for consonance. When a plucked string gives forth a musical sound, corresponding in pitch to its length, acute listeners can recognize the simultaneous presence of feebler tones of higher pitch. Mersenne, for example, recorded the detection of four such overtones: the octave higher, a fifth above that, the next octave, and its major third.

It was Sauveur, the Father of Acoustics as he is some-times called, who applied the term harmonics to these higher tones which accompany the lower tone, or fun-damental. It was he also, who gave the first satisfactory explanation for their presence. The musical tone emitted by a string is not pure but is complex, with components which are on the whole mutually conso-nant. What reaches the ear is a series of pure tones— a wave train bearing on its back little waves, and the little waves have lesser waves, and so ad infinitum. And he proved this in a simple conclusive manner.

Bowing a stretched string so as to produce its char-acteristic tone when vibrating as a whole, he touched it gently with a feather at its center so as to damp out that vibration, while permitting the separate halves to continue such vibrations as they were already engaged in. In the absence of the deeper note of the funda-mental, the octave was then easily evident. In a similar manner, checking the vibration at one-third the length, he showed that the string was vibrating also in three segments, each giving out a tone of three times the frequency of the fundamental. The second octave, four times as high in frequency, was heard when he elimi-nated the three lower tones by enforcing quiescence upon the particles of the string at one-quarter its length. Whatever the frequency of the fundamental note may be there are present tones two, three, four, and so on times higher in frequency; the tone is a com-plex of component pure tones the frequencies of which are proportional to 1, 2, 3, 4, 5, 6, and so on.

In the description of this fact the musician and the electrical engineer are inclined to part company. Since the latter usually deals with the series on a mathematical basis, where it is convenient to think of the third term, for example, as the one representing three times the fundamental frequency, he falls into the habit of describing it as the third harmonic. To the musician, unfortunately, the third term in the series is the second overtone or harmonic. But the worst of the confusion lies in the fact that the musician thinks of the series as C_1, C_2, G_2, C_3, E_3, G_3; and when he speaks of an harmonic he means a note with all the overtones which accompany it. His harmonics are not pure.

That a single note on a musical instrument is a complex sound involving a series of components of higher frequency was an important discovery. It led immediately to an explanation of why musical notes, identical in pitch, should sound differently when played on different instruments. The quality of any sound depends upon the pure ingredients from which it is compounded and upon their relative strengths. If the sound is musical its pitch is that of the fundamental pure tone. Identity of pitch, in other words, means merely identity for the fundamental components; and promises nothing as to the overtones. A piano and a violin give rise to similar series but their corresponding components do not have the same relative strength as compared to their fundamentals; hence the two instruments are easily distinguishable. A violin and a clarinet have a different series of components; in one case, 1, 2, 3, 4, 5, 6, and in the other 1, 3, 5, 6, 7, 8, and so on. The difference in quality is correspondingly more marked.

The quality, or timbre as it is sometimes called, of a sound may be quantitatively described by stating the frequencies and intensities of its several components. With the acceptance of this idea there started a succession of researches into the character, or composition, of all types of sound. The sounds of bells and of vibrating plates, for which the overtones are not harmonics, the sounds of speech, which are not only complex but transient, and, more recently, noise have all been carefully studied; over and over again as more refined laboratory techniques have permitted correspondingly more accurate determination.

Until telephonic, and other electrical, equipment became available these investigations were carried out through the use of two types of apparatus, both mechanical and both with modern equivalents in electrical equipment. One of these, corresponding to the oscilloscope which will be described in a later chapter, gave a picture of a complex sound in the form of a wavy line of light. The other, an invention of the famous Helmholtz about the middle of the nineteenth century, consisted of a series of resonators, each adapted to respond most sensitively to sound waves of a single frequency. These were hollow spheres, each with a fairsized opening through which the sound could enter and, on the opposite side, an outlet through a small nipple for the ear of the observer. With such resonators Helmholtz made careful analyses of the component tones of many types of complex sounds.

His researches covered the entire field of acoustics and are fundamental to much of our modern knowledge of speech and music and of the performance of the human ear. The ear, for example, had shown a preference for the Pythagorean ratios, but during the

succeeding 2500 years there had appeared no acceptable explanation. Helmholtz demonstrated that the
phenomena of consonance and dissonance were due to
the ear's reaction to the overtones in the complex
sounds with which Pythagoras experimented. When
one note has overtones which are in unison with those
of another note, then the ear is pleased; and the more
so, the larger the number of components which are in
unison. Strings, for example, a fifth apart, will have
unison between four overtones of their first twelve
component tones.

Dissonance, on the other hand, is explained as due
to an inherent objection on the part of the ear to conflicting demands upon its attention, by some of the
overtones. Picture the eardrum as a sidewalk upon
which there pace together two persons whose lengths
of step differ. The impacts which their feet make with
the sidewalk correspond to the pressures which the air
molecules exert against the eardrum when two pure
sounds of different frequency are heard. If the frequencies, with which the walkers raise and lower their feet,
differ but slightly—their paces almost equal—then, from
time to time they will be in step and exert a maximum
of pressure on the sidewalk. The corresponding ear
recognizes a recurrent swelling of the total tone, "beats"
as they are called. If the frequencies have a greater numerical difference the beats become more rapid until
they merge into an annoying flutter and produce the
familiar grating sensation of dissonance. If they occur
still more rapidly the annoyance disappears. The parallel is, then, that of an adult with a long stride and a
child running beside him: the sounds no longer conflict.

2 ELECTRICAL EARS

A cherished exhibit in the museum of the Bell Telephone System is a small square of smoked glass. Its carbon coating shows a fine wavy scratch, from which in 1874 Bell concluded that the telephone he was trying to invent must produce an "undulatory" electrical current. In modern terms the glass plate is an oscillogram—a picture of a wave.

The oscillograph, with which Bell obtained it, was formed in part by the human ear of a cadaver. Attached to the inner surface of the eardrum was a fine straw, the other end of which rested on the smoked glass. When one spoke to this ear its drum vibrated and the straw moved back and forth, tracing a short line in the smoke. The character of the motion was made evident when the plate was given an additional motion at right angles to this trace. Try to draw a straight line back and forth across a sheet of paper while you pull the sheet lengthwise; and you will see how Bell disclosed the nature of the vibration which speech establishes in the ear.

In life the eardrum responds to the delicate touch; just how readily can be appreciated from the following rule for testing one's hearing in the home. Tear an ordinary sheet of business letter paper—these run about seven to the ounce—into forty equal pieces. Take one of these and divide it into a thousand equal parts.

Repeat the process with one of these. Of course, if one's precision of workmanship is sufficient these operations can be shortened, since it is only necessary to snip off a fortieth of a millionth part of the original sheet. Next, lie on the side so that the ear is horizontal and let this snip of paper rest on the eardrum. Lifting it slightly, lower it gently—you must not let it fall—until it rests again. Repeat this regularly a thousand times a second. If the ear action is normal there can just be perceived a tone about two octaves above middle C.

The eardrum, as its name implies, is a thin elastic membrane under tension. In this respect it is similar to the diaphragm of microphones, that is telephone transmitters, and of telephone receivers, whether loud speakers or not. In addition to its remarkable sensitivity it possesses, in common with such devices, the ability to respond to more than one sound wave at a time. If it could not—if it could only vibrate at one frequency at a time—there would be neither music nor speech as we now know them.

For any stretched diaphragm, the distinction must be drawn between vibrations which are natural to it and those which are forced upon it. If you have a drum handy and a little fine dry sand you can make a qualitative demonstration of natural vibrations. Sprinkle a thin layer of sand on its head and hit it one beat. As it vibrates the sand will shake into a pattern of ridges. Where there is the least sand the motion has been the greatest; the ridges mark the nodal lines where the vibration is least. The drum head, in other words, vibrates in a number of different modes, simultaneously.

When violently deformed by a blow it swings back toward its normal position but overshoots its mark and is almost as badly off as before for it is again deformed, although in the opposite sense. And so it vibrates back and forth until it has used up all the energy stored in it by the blow. The original deformation is only momentary; thereafter, the membrane adopts modes of vibration which are characteristic and natural to itself. Its behavior is like that of a stretched string which has been plucked; it vibrates in a complex manner with different parts carrying on at different frequencies.

Forced vibrations, on the other hand, are like the shaking of a child by an angry adult: they take place in accordance with the force and as long as it is applied. When application ceases the child may go into some convulsive movements of its own but these are natural in that they represent its own attempt to restore its equilibrium. Natural vibrations always ensue when an elastic body is left to itself to recover from some displacement; but forced vibrations occur only while a periodic force is applied.

The function of the eardrum is to transmit to the inner mechanism the vibrations which it is forced to pick up from the adjacent medium of the air. In the air also the vibrations are forced: each molecule must move to accommodate itself to the motion of others still nearer to the sound source. When the wave is traced back to the original source it will be found that there the vibrations are natural and free, whether they arise from a musical instrument, are vocal, or are merely noise. They may result from human actions but they take place after the act and not during it.

A pianist strikes a key and a padded hammer falls upon a string, producing a sharply localized deformation. The elasticity of the string and the inertia of its particles then assume responsibility for the complex tone which ensues and for all its components. When a violinist draws a rosined bow across a string of his instrument he pulls the string away from its normal position of rest until its elastic self-restoring force, which increases with the displacement, wrenches it loose from the friction grip of the bow. Natural vibrations then occur. Between the piano string and that of the violin the essential difference in excitation is that for one it is accomplished by a single strong push, once and for all, while for the other by a succession of small pulls.

For wind instruments the case is illustrated by the larynx. When speech or song is to be produced the larynx tightens, restricting the passage of the air which the diaphragm would expel. The pressure rises until the larynx, which is a pair of lips, is pushed apart and air is allowed to escape. The consequent reduction in air pressure allows the larynx to fly back and to engage for an instant in its natural vibrations. Only for an instant, however, for the rising pressure again breaks through and the cycle repeats, so that the natural vibrations are sustained as long as the pressure is kept up. In this regard they are similar to those of a violin string which continue while the bow acts.

In wind instruments the place of the larynx is taken by a reed, or by a thin lip,[1] or by the lips of the per-

---

[1] In the case of an organ pipe the lip does not vibrate. It serves as a fulcrum on which teeters the stream of air which blows the pipe. When this stream first enters the pipe it compresses the air imme-

former which are a close parallel in their action to the larynx itself. Of the complex sounds which these vibrations represent some components are favored by resonance in the neighboring chambers of air.

For the vocal organs these actions are well illustrated by the so-called "artificial larynx", which was developed for the aid of patients who had undergone a laryngectomy. Its essential element is a metal cylinder about as big as a restaurant salt-cellar with a nipple at each end to which can be attached rubber tubes of about the diameter of a pencil. Within is a rubber membrane which is set into vibration when a current of air passes through the device. How that air stream is supplied by one who has lost his physiological larynx would require speaking of operations. The device, however, is conveniently demonstrated with air from a bellows. A push-button valve allows the stream of air to escape except when it is wanted to set up the natural vibrations of the larynx.

These vibrations are complex. They emit from the tube a raucous "ah" which contains a number of component sounds not all consonant with each other. The

diately in front of it; and this in turn the air farther along in the pipe. A pulse of compression, therefore, travels down the pipe with the velocity usual for such motion, that is, with the velocity of sound. At the distant end the pulse reflects and returns. When it gets back it adds its congestion to that imposed by the entering stream upon the molecules of air nearest it. This proves a little too much for the stream and it seeks a less congested region just outside the lip. As it does so it creates a slight reduction of air pressure—a partial vacuum— and this rarefaction proceeds up and back in the pipe. Upon its return it adds its partial vacuum to that already existing. And now the stream finds so much less resistance inside the pipe that it flips back and the entire process repeats. The periodicity with which it does so is controlled by the time of travel up and down.

tube is stuck in the mouth and there supplies sounds near enough like those of the human larynx so that easily intelligible speech is possible. It is only necessary to shape the mouth for the desired syllables and to position tongue, teeth, and lips as nearly as the tube permits. Certain of the component sounds are thereby enhanced through resonance. No new sounds are created; all that is accomplished is a selection from the component pure tones which arise from the natural vibrations of the artificial larynx.

What is true of music and speech is also of noise. It is due, in general, to the natural vibrations of its sources. Drop a pencil on a hard floor, tap a window pane, or pound the desk, if you want, and natural vibrations ensue. When that is not true the noise is due to a succession of impulses like the "plop, plop" of dripping water; but in this case, as the characterization of the sound implies, there are some vibrations. The best instance of a succession of impulses happens to be those established by the siren which was mentioned in the preceding chapter. In the siren a rotating disc, with a regular series of holes, allows a series of puffs to escape from a jet of compressed air. Because they occur regularly and at a fairly high frequency the sound is musical rather than noise. On the other hand, the familiar "putt-putt" of a motor boat gets its characteristic from the natural frequencies of parts of the engine or boat.

Between the ear and a source of sound there must be some continuous medium in which forced vibrations may follow those of the source. Imagine a crowd surging close to the scene of a street accident and driven back—if it is—by the cry of "Give him air". Again it surges closer. Each movement is transmitted outward in expanding circles. When those nearest the scene push back, they crowd those behind them who in turn crowd those behind; and so a pulse of condensation travels radially outward through the crowd. When those nearest step forward they increase the space between themselves and others immediately behind. The latter promptly close in; and so a pulse of rarefaction proceeds outward. A similar succession of movements is imposed upon the molecules of air adjacent to a source of sound. If the vibrations of the source are periodic a train of waves results, alternate condensations and rarefactions, which are repeated with exactness but with decreasing amplitudes in succeeding layers of air.

That is a picture of the wave motion corresponding to a single-frequency vibration, to a pure note. Strictly speaking, what takes place is that each particle of air vibrates back and forth with a motion identical to that of a pendulum bob except that it occurs along a straight line, radially outward from the source, instead of along the arc of a circle. Such motion is known as simple harmonic. It is completely determined by its frequency, that is the number of cycles per second, and by its amplitude, that is the maximum displacement from its normal position or point of rest. The vibration is most conveniently described by a term that has a trigonometric origin, "sinusoidal", which derives from the same root as "sinuous" and represents the simplest, and most regular, wavy line.

A particle of air can transmit simultaneously and faithfully a number of sinusoidal motions. Imagine a shuttle train running back and forth, without waiting for passengers, between Times Square and Grand Central. In the train a man walks back and forth from one end to the other. He swings a bird cage in his hand, on the perch of which swings a canary. Picture its motion, which is the resultant of four periodic motions, and you have a faint perception of the complexity of motion of each molecule of air which intervenes between your ears and a symphony orchestra in the simplest acoustic situation when there is a solo part. A similar vibration is imposed upon your eardrum by the adjacent molecules of air. Now extend this image to cover the entire complex of musical tones from a full orchestra, each with its series of overtones and each originating at a different location on the stage. That is an extreme illustration of what the ear must pick up in the way of vibratory motions. How the vibrations then proceed from eardrum to brain is another story, not all of which is known.

The sound from an orchestra is a group of component sounds, each a sinusoidal vibration, of which the frequency tells the pitch; and the amplitude, the intensity. It is upon the amplitude that loudness depends, but unfortunately for easy exposition, it does not do so directly. Along the route from orchestra to eardrum intervening particles must engage simultaneously in forced vibrations with frequencies corresponding to all these sinusoidal components. Particles far distant from the source, however, will not have the same amplitude of vibration as those nearer. As the sound spreads out it must attenuate because the area over which it is distributed increases as the square of the distance it has traveled.

Doubling the distance quarters the acoustic energy which will fall upon the ear. If a program is held up from an orchestra seat fifty feet from a soloist it intercepts four times the acoustic energy which it would at a hundred feet and sixteen times as much as for two hundred feet. At least that would be the case in the Rose Bowl; in an auditorium the walls reflect back some of the energy and the reduction with distance is not quite so severe. In a hall none of the energy escapes; it is merely reflected back and forth until it is finally absorbed in upholstery and hangings, in the clothes of the auditors and, in small part, in their ears.

Attenuation is an inevitable accompaniment of transmission. As a sound wave proceeds the amplitudes of its sinusoidal motions grow less. All the component sinusoids must suffer similar reduction in amplitude, if the character of the music is to be preserved. There must be no favoritism for the amplitudes of those components which happen to have certain frequencies. But even in free air there is some partiality; the tones of higher frequency suffer most in transmission. In halls equivalent effects of discrimination may be obtained due to walls or hangings which may selectively absorb some vibrations. Such effects, however, are a matter of auditorium acoustics which demands a later chapter by itself. Of present importance is the fact that for distortionless transmission there must be established at each successive point between sound source and ear similar complex vibrations. All components must suffer the same percentage reduction in amplitude so that the original relationship is preserved.

It was Alexander Graham Bell's idea to introduce between sound source and ear an electrical system which could transmit the vibrations essential to speech but with much smaller attenuation than would occur if the medium were entirely air.

It is within the limits of possibility that if Bell had had the data which are today available as to the characteristics of speech he would have been discouraged from his attempt. The wide range of frequencies involved in the sounds of speech, the number of component sinusoids in its complex sounds and the tiny amount of power in a spoken syllable might have made the telephone seem an impossibility. To a certain extent Bell was protected in his faith by his own ignorance and that of his time. That he could have known the delicate complexity which he was trying to transmit is a condition contrary to fact, because much of the information has been disclosed by researches in which later forms of his instrument were utilized.

What Bell invented was first of all an electrical ear. A diaphragm corresponding to the eardrum is forced into vibration by the air waves of speech. Within the human ear a complicated mechanism translates into nerve impulses what the drum picks up. Within Bell's transmitter a relatively simple mechanism translated the variations of pressure in the air wave into variations of electrical current. A wire circuit—the first telephone line—allowed the current to flow to the distant receiving apparatus. This was in effect an electrical mouth since it could utter the sounds which the electric ear had heard. It was a translating device whereby variations of current produced corresponding variations of pressure in the surrounding air.

In the course of his experiments Bell disclosed three of the four possible ways by which air waves falling on an electrical ear can be converted into an undulatory current. The fourth method was soon discovered by another inventor but had no practical application until, years later, in Bell Telephone Laboratories, it was perfected and embodied in the so-called condenser-transmitter. This device, which was originally developed as a laboratory tool in the investigation of speech and music and of the sensitivity of human hearing, became the famous "mike" of broadcasting and sound pictures.

The operation of translating sound waves into electrical is most easily explained for the transmitter of the ordinary telephone set. Behind its diaphragm is a small chamber, or "button", partially filled with fine grains of carbon which have been prepared by crushing and roasting coal. As the diaphragm vibrates, under the varying pressure of the molecules of air which carry the sound wave, the mass of carbon is alternately compressed slightly or allowed to expand. During compression its particles make broader contact with each other, just as two tennis balls touch over a larger area if crowded together. When the grains are more closely packed the button offers less resistance to the passage through it of an electrical current. It therefore affords a mechanism for varying a current in conformity with the motion of a diaphragm. Current is supplied to the button by a battery; and except as the diaphragm moves its amount is unchanged. When the diaphragm is set into vibration there are introduced into the current variations which correspond in frequency and are proportional in amplitude.

Only the ups and downs of current have significance; into them are metamorphosed the vocal sounds which fall upon the transmitter. At the receiving end of the telephone line this magic must be undone. It is not necessary to transmit the entire current which flows through the button, if only there may be made available at the distant receiver a current similar in its variations, one in which they have the same relative amplitude and occur at the same frequency.

Into the circuit formed by the battery and carbon button, therefore, is inserted one winding of a transformer—a piece of equipment operating on the same principle as the iron pots which connect house mains to the pole lines of electric light companies. The varying current then flows from battery to button, through that, through the transformer winding and back to the battery. In the transformer, on the same magnetizable core, is another, or secondary, winding. To this is connected the pair of wires which leads to the receiver. In this second circuit no current flows as long as the current in the first remains steady. It is the peculiarity, however, of the transformer that any change of current in the first winding immediately induces a current in the second. If in the primary winding there is a periodically varying current there will be established in the secondary an alternating current. This will flow first in one direction and then in the other, with its alternations in time with the increases and decreases of the primary current. In the secondary circuit, therefore, is a current with frequency equal to that of the periodic variations in the primary and with amplitude proportional.

Through the use of such a transformer there is obtained from the circuit which includes the carbon button just the current that is essential for the electrical transmission of the sound. If the vibrations of the diaphragm are complex, then of similar complexity will be the current variations through the button; and the secondary current will involve similar variations. In the ideal case it will contain sinusoidal components corresponding to each of the sinusoidal components in the vibratory motion of the molecules in the original sound wave.

To translate these components of current into sound waves there is employed at the distant station another device with a diaphragm. In the simplest case its diaphragm, which is made of magnetic material, is bowed slightly by the attraction of a magnet. Around the magnet is wound a coil of wire in which flows the current with its sound-bearing alternations. The current, then, alternately helps and hinders the magnet in its attraction for the diaphragm. And so the latter vibrates back and forth with a period and an amplitude corresponding to the current.

The sound which the electrical ear hears is thus reproduced. But more than that: the sound wave has been converted into an electrical wave and as such is susceptible to manipulation, to measurement, to amplification, to distortion or correction, and to amazing processes almost innumerable.

It was Robert Louis Stevenson, in the essay where he confessed an unwillingness to share bed and board with an early riser and a vegetarian, who first made clear to at least one person the importance in human relations of identical definitions for the common words of everyday life. Scales and accepted standards are necessary: a base from which to start measurement and an ascending or descending series of steps.

For most magnitudes the simplest base from which to start is zero; and the easiest steps are equal. Whether it is time or distance, pounds sterling or avoirdupois, we are accustomed to start from zero and to count in unit steps. A distance may be expressed in miles or in kilometers, but whatever these numbers may be they will each be twice as great for double the distance. There is a rationality to such a scale; but there are other scales which are not so simple although entirely rational and in certain situations much more convenient.

Imagine, for example, the owner of a fishing preserve who might with some justice describe his piscatorial wealth in terms of the amount of fishing which had, or had not been, done in the various pools. This pool had not been fished for five years; and that for three. The fish in any pool increase on a percentage basis and the number present bears a definite ratio to the number of inhabitants of the same pool the year before. It matters little what the reference point is.

Somewhat of that character is the musician's unit in his various scales. It is about as definitive as the unit of a year's freedom from fishing, in that each higher note represents a certain percentage increase in frequency; but it is justifiable and convenient.

The musician always had a hard time deciding with how many trout to stock his pool. In church music in Mersenne's time the A above middle C was as low as 374 vibrations per second; for chamber music it was 403. It got up to 422 in Handel's time and as high as 460 in New York; and was standardized at 444 by German physicists in the early nineteenth century. The Diapason normal of French pitch was 435—as accurately measured by Koenig it turned out to be 435.45 cycles per second—and this was called the "international pitch", from which scale measurements should be made.

The nomenclature was somewhat inexact because it was never universally accepted. About 1925 the musical industry in America decided to standardize on 440; and since then that has been its "standard pitch". The Germans took to 439; the French held on to 435; the English adopted 440. If A is 440 the C above is 523.2.

Physicists, who are perhaps less temperamentally agile than musicians, adopted a pitch of 512 as the octave above middle C. The difference is small and the arithmetical simplicity considerable. Today, with music going electrical, there is coming into general use a reference value of 1000 cycles per second which has been •
found convenient by the electrical engineer in the com-

munication arts. It has no musical name and is merely a standardized and easily reproducible frequency about which more will be said later.

After a standard of frequency has been chosen any other frequency may be described by its scaled distance above or below. The universally adopted scale defines the interval between two frequencies as their ratio. For certain ratios, particularly those which occur in music, names have evolved and been accepted. Thus the ratio 2/1 is the octave, 3/2 the fifth, 5/4 the major third, 9/8 the major tone, 10/9 the minor tone and 16/15 the diatonic semitone. Starting with any frequency the octaves successively above it will have frequencies 2, 4, 8, 16, and 32 times higher; and those below 1/2, 1/4, 1/8 and so on.

If the interval between some note t and another u is $m/1$; and if an interval of $n/1$ above u there is another note v, then the entire interval between t and v is found by multiplying the ratios representing the two intermediate intervals; and so is $mn/1$. A concrete illustration of this arithmetic of intervals is the case where the first ratio is 9/8 and the next 10/9; the product of these is 9×10 divided by 8×9, that is 5/4; or in words, two successive steps on the diatonic scale, one a major tone and the other a minor tone, are equivalent to the single step of a so-called major third.

The terminology of the musician, at least as concerns intervals, is the unfortunate product of evolution. He uses the word "tone" to represent not only a musical sound but also the interval between two such sounds. His tones, too, may be either single sinusoidal vibrations or complex with several component sinusoids. An interval like the major third he named because it happened to be the step between the first and third notes of his major scale. A more logical and not less useful terminology could undoubtedly be contrived, and one which would tend to indicate rather than to obscure the fundamentally important numerical ratios. Its adoption and common use might, of course, be a socially difficult operation.

The intervals of music have relatively little importance to the electrical engineer who devises or operates systems for the transmission of music or for its recording. To him are of interest those larger intervals which embrace all the usual notes of music and their overtones. Such larger steps he sometimes refers to as "bands of frequencies", stating the width of the band in cycles per second. He would describe a radio set, for example, by stating the band of frequencies which it can reproduce. If this extended from 100 cycles per second to 4000 it would cover an interval of 4000/100, that is 40/1. A range of five octaves covers the interval 32/1; to the major third above would be an added interval of 5/4. Adding the interval 32/1 and 5/4 gives a total interval of $32 \times 5/4$ or 40/1. Such a radio set, therefore, covers five octaves and a major third; approximately all fundamental tones from G_1 to about C_7. Its inability to transmit tones of higher frequency means that some overtones, of notes whose fundamentals lie within its range, will not get through. Since the first overtone is the octave of its fundamental, notes above C_6 will lack all overtones; notes between C_5 and C_6 will be accompanied by only one or two; those below C_4 will have practically all their important overtones.

The transmission range of any device, or system, which is to be employed in the transmission, or reproduction, of music should always be stated in terms of the band of frequencies which it will handle. Only in that way is exactness possible; description in terms of glowing adjectives, or specially coined words, is meaningless where it is not misleading; even specification in terms of the tones or notes which are reproduced is not conclusive because these words are ambiguous as to whether or not overtones are included.

After the frequency range of an electro-acoustical device has been stated there still remains the question of how faithfully it will perform within that range. Will it transmit, or translate, all components of a sound equally well? Will all the component sinusoids emerge with intensities in the same proportion to their original intensities in the complex sound or current? Will a radio receiving set, for example, reproduce without distortion what it receives from the broadcasting station? In its turn will the radio transmitter deliver to the set in the same relative proportions all the sinusoidal components in the current it receives from the microphone? And will that instrument faithfully pick up and translate the complex sound waves of the studio? Experimental analysis will determine at each point along the route from performer to auditor.

For such tests some scale of measurement is required and the "decibel" scale of the communication engineer is now generally accepted. By its use comparisons may be conveniently expressed; acoustic power, or its electrical equivalent while in process of transmission, may be referred to some standard and quantitatively described as so many units above or below the standard.

The unit is the "bel", named after the inventor of the telephone; but its submultiple, the euphonious "decibel", abbreviated "db", is much more commonly used. It does not stand for any definite amount of power but rather for a specific percentage increment. In the transmission of music, as will be developed more fully later, the absolute amount of power is usually not as important as the ratio to some other power. In the pianissimo portions of an orchestral rendering it is not the actual amount of power which passes through the proscenium arch which counts but rather the ratio which that power bears to the room and audience noise which would mask it. In electrical apparatus for transmitting sound the ratio between the power which emerges and that which enters is of primary interest.

Such ratios are measured on the decibel scale. This scale and that for pitch are similar in all respects except one. They have in common the conception of successively higher and higher levels, in one case of frequency and in the other of power. Both scales measure differences in level, expressing the ratio of one level to the other. In either case it is possible to choose some particular ratio, expressing some definite difference in level, as the unit in terms of which all intervals between levels may be expressed.

So far there is similarity but when it comes to choosing a unit the musician behaves like an Anglo-Saxon in weights and measures. He uses pounds and tons, ounces, grams and drams with all their illogical relationships. There must be tones and semitones, fifths, thirds, sixths, even sevenths, and most of these must have their major and minor qualifications. For difference in level of powers, on the other hand, there is a single unit, the decibel, more definitive in value than the dollar but like it capable of decimal subdivision if necessary.

This unit has a perfect mathematical justification, which will not be stressed because its appreciation demands dealing with logarithms, and an approximate psychological basis.

A well-known law of psychology, the Weber-Fechner law, states a general relationship between increase of stimulus and resulting increase of sensation. In audition, however, there are interesting departures. Remember how a band sounds in a parade. As it gets nearer the bass comes out more strongly although its musicians do not alter their playing. As the band approaches all its sound waves reach the ear with greater intensity; at half the distance away their acoustic power at the ear is quadrupled because the intensity varies inversely as the square of the distance. Treble and bass both increase as the band comes nearer, but as they become more intense the low notes seem disproportionately louder. Equal increases in stimulus do not, therefore, produce equal increases in the sensation of loudness. The law does not hold exactly; on the other hand, in the middle range of audible pitches the ear does follow the law closely enough to justify a comparison unit based approximately on sensation.

The law deals with the increase in stimulus which is necessary to produce a discernible increase in sensation. Imagine that one listens alternately to two musical notes identical in pitch and for the moment of equal intensity. Then one of the sounds is slightly increased and the comparison repeated; and so on, until to the ear the notes appear to differ in loudness. The minimum perceptible difference in intensity is thus determined for the conditions of the experiment, that is, for a definite pitch of note and a definite initial sensation.

Repeat the experiment, keeping the stronger of the two tones steady and increasing the intensity of the other until it is just perceptibly louder. Another level of sensation is thus attained. Approximately it will satisfy the Weber law that the intensity of the stimulus necessary for any sensation level can be obtained by multiplying the intensity for the level immediately lower by a definite constant factor. Successive sensations, in other words, arise from stimuli the values of which form a series that increases like the value of a bank account under compound interest. It grows by steps which are constant portions of the preceding value.

The difference in loudness of any two sounds can be measured by the number of intermediate steps necessary to pass from the level of the lesser sound to that of the other. The average increase in acoustic power which the ear can detect is about twenty-five percent. On that basis each level corresponds to a power 1.25 times that of the next lower level. Assuming, for convenience, that the power at some level is 10, then the powers of successively higher levels are: 10; 12.5; 16; 20; 25; 32; 40; 50; 63; 80; and 100. The series extends indefinitely to higher and lower values; for example, the next higher terms are 125; 160; 200; and so on.

Each level in the series represents a step of one decibel. Ten steps and one is on a power level ten times that from which he started, a whole bel higher. The reference level may be the choice, or necessity, of the moment just as is the tonic of the musician; but starting from that level the scale of decibels proceeds in the same way by steps. Just as on the scale of frequency two successive steps, each a "tone", mean a total interval of a major third and a corresponding frequency ratio of 5/4, so two successive decibels mean a total interval of two decibels and the corresponding ratio of 16/10. The decibel scale takes ten steps to reach the level beyond which the ratios reoccur; the pitch scale (diatonic) takes eight. The third on the power scale corresponds to the ratio 20/10; that is, power doubles every three decibels.

Where the musician chooses some pitch for his keynote the engineer tends to take what he can find. In the discussion of the acoustic power in speech, for example, he may take the average as "zero level". His measurements then show that very loud speech is about 20 db higher; it is therefore said to have a level of +20 db. Very faint speech is 20 db below the arbitrarily chosen level of reference, that is at —20 db. Ordinarily, then, speech covers a "volume", or power, range of 40 db. Since for every ten decibels power increases ten times, this range represents an increase of ten thousand times. When one argues his acoustic power is probably, therefore, about ten thousand times greater than it need be.

A whisper is about 20 db below faint speech and represents a power about one ten-thousandth that of ordinary speech, and a millionth that of loud speech. The human ear must have a wide range of adaptability to respond to such different intensities of speech sounds, but that is another story for a later chapter. It is sufficient for the moment to say that if the lips of an average speaker are held within a half inch of the ear of a person of normal hearing, the acoustic power which the ear receives is ten billion times greater (100 db higher in level) than the ear needs for the mere perception of the sound.

With such a range of power in ordinary speech and with such amazing sensitivity on the part of the ear it is evident that a matter of two or three decibels may, at times, be a mere trifle. Although a change in acoustic power of less than one db is perceptible under laboratory conditions, twice as much is about the least trained observers can detect under ordinary conditions. The adjusting dials on equipment are generally calibrated, or arranged to adjust, in steps of three db. If a phonograph is playing dance music in the living room and, while one is out of the room, its acoustic power is changed by three db—and that means either doubling or halving the power output—it is doubtful if the change could be appreciated upon one's return.

That means that if one should listen to the same short phrase played first under one condition and then under another, and so on alternately, a difference in power level of two or three decibels for the two conditions would be about as little as one might expect to detect. If such a difference in level occurred only in some of the notes and some of the higher overtones it would probably escape any except the most expert attention.

In the design, or test, of a piece of electro-acoustic equipment, or of a whole system from transmitter to receiver, the engineer makes a comparison, throughout the frequency range which is to be handled, between power output and power input. He finds for each frequency what the decibel difference is. If it is the same for all frequencies he ascribes to the device a "flat characteristic". He uses this term because the results of his observations are plotted, like a curve of stock prices against successive days, in decibels versus frequency. No change, and the plot is a straight line. Although his curves never approach the irregularity of price curves they do as a rule bend down a little at the lower frequencies and even more at the higher, being approximately flat in the middle range of frequencies.

If the plot is not flat there is a distortion during transmission through the device; some sinusoidal components are more generously treated than others; in general, an entire range of components suffer. Knowing from his plot the maximum discrimination which occurs the engineer then describes the apparatus as having a transmission characteristic "flat to within so many db over such and such a range of frequencies". If the number of db by which the transmission of various frequencies differs is only two or three the apparatus is practically distortionless, despite the fact that some sinusoids may have less than half the power they should.

By the use of two scales, for frequency and power, both based on ratios, there can be adequately described any acoustical, or electro-acoustical, system. More and more, musicians, especially those who come in contact with communication engineers, are adopting the easy terminology of the decibel scale. Time may even come when it will be used by composers and scores will no longer be marked with *pp* and *ff*. Pianissimo may then be zero level, indicating the softest music which will fit the condition of auditorium acoustics and audience noise; and all higher levels will be marked in corresponding numbers of db. Certainly the composers who write the music for the electrical musical instruments of the future will need to specify the desired intensity in terms easily followed by the controllers of the current.

PART TWO

TELEPHONIC STUDIES OF HEARING

On the morning of All Fools' Day, 1911, I started to work for the American Telephone and Telegraph Company in its engineering department in New York. A few minutes later, I was on my first assignment—a purely complimentary one, intended for the training of a hybrid between physicist and cub transmission engineer. "Go down to the terminal room," my chief said, "and see what you think of the transmission to Denver. We're opening that circuit to commercial service tomorrow."

A few engineers were taking turns in talking to their fellows in Denver. They were the experts of their day in judgment of telephone transmission; and they were giving the line its final talking tests before it passed into the hands of plant and traffic departments for maintenance and operation. I had no basis of comparison because my experience in telephoning had been limited to city or suburban distances.

I did not find Denver within easy talking distance. Three years later, while we were extending that line to San Francisco and I was following it back and forth making measurements, I plugged in on the test board at Salt Lake and called home to New Jersey. I had a hard time persuading my wife, so clear did my voice sound, that I wasn't on my way back and at least in Pittsburgh if not already in New York. Between 1911 and 1914 there had occurred in telephony a scientific revolution.

The line to Denver had been built with extra large wires so as to offer to the passage of the current the least feasible resistance. The insulators which supported its wires on the crossarms of the poles had been designed to reduce to a minimum the leaking of current from one wire of the pair to the other, or its diversion in wet weather along the pole to the ground. Every eight miles carefully designed "loading coils" were connected into the line. These were heavy coils of wire, wound on iron cores; and their spacing along the line followed the patented formula which Michael I. Pupin had sold to the telephone company a few years before. Their effect is to reduce the attenuation—the progressive enfeeblement—which alternating currents must suffer in transmission. Under the best of conditions, loading just about doubles the efficiency of a line, permitting the same grade of telephonic transmission as for an ordinary line half as long. By applying loading Denver, rather than Chicago, had become the most Western point within speaking distance of New York.

In the engineering of that line all the techniques then available had been employed; and the result was the longest practicable telephone line. A definite limit had been reached; only so far could the engineers advance in their conflict with the natural forces of attenuation. For telephony over longer distances a new instrument was required—not a new terminal instrument, for simple reasons [1] which need not be given here, but something which could be connected into the circuit

[1] Cf. "Signals and Speech in Electrical Communication", pp. 240-1.

at an intermediate city to amplify the speech-bearing currents before they became too much attenuated.

The solution is obvious: use a vacuum tube as an amplifier, just as we do in our radio sets. But in those relatively nearby times there was no radio telephony which got any distance; and no vacuum tubes; and no technical information which would be helpful. There was almost nothing which would serve; but there was a research spirit in the engineering corps and a number of men hired as the nucleus of a research department. For a time this group concentrated its efforts on the single problem of transcontinental telephony.

Three different methods were developed and all successfully met the test of commercial service. One of them offered almost limitless possibilities: that was the vacuum-tube telephone repeater. It was developed through the researches of the late H. D. Arnold from the audion which Lee DeForest had invented some years earlier as a detector of radio signals. His device in its turn was an important advance on one which Fleming in England had invented, usefully employing a phenomenon that Edison had observed in his early experiments on incandescent lamps. The history of this development,[1] and of its final interpretation by the United States Supreme Court, is a story of more than scientific interest.

For present purposes the essential of the story is that Arnold developed a high-vacuum three-electrode thermionic tube; and that device acting as an amplifier, and supported by the results of a number of other researches, made possible transcontinental wire-teleph-

[1] Cf. "The Modern Jinn", Chapter 10, "Signals and Speech".

ony and the opening in 1915 of a circuit between New York and San Franciso. During those years of 1912-5, the whole picture of long-distance telephony was changed for its engineers. In the wasting disease of attenuation the vacuum-tube telephone repeater became the specific. Whereas loading could only reduce the rate at which the energy of an electrical wave was dissipated in its travels, the repeater could supply new life and energy. Attenuation was conquered and the transmission of speech and music became physically possible over any route where wires could be strung.

Where wires would be impracticable speech would have to go by radio. In those days there was telegraphy by radio. Most ships had their sputtering spark-sets which set up high-frequency currents in the antenna when the operator pressed the key. Key down for a moment and he sent a dot; down about three times as long, a dash. Sometimes, today, these signals may be heard in the midst of a radio program, breaking through with the . . . — — — . . . of the SOS or with other codes. Telephony by radio had been tried but with no success except over almost negligible distances.

There was a basic reason for this failure. In any transmission of information whether by arbitrarily coded signals, as in telegraphy, or by the evolved code of language, as in telephony, there are four essential operations to be performed.[1] First, there must be the generation of some "effect" which can be transmitted;

[1] Authors in submitting manuscripts have been known to stick together the middle pages of their offerings to check on the perusal of the publishers' readers. It is not usual to apply such suspicious methods to printed pages. Nevertheless, when this text becomes too detailed or technical for any reader its author could wish the inter-

next, its variation, or modulation, in conformity with the signal or speech; then, the transmission of this modulated effect; and finally, at the distant terminal demodulation to obtain from the variations the information they involve.

In wire telegraphy the effect was the current from a battery; this was varied by a key; and the arrival of the variation at the other end of the line was manifested by a sounder, a simple electromagnet which pulled up its armature with a click when current arrived and allowed it to fall back with a clack when current ceased to flow. For telephony there was the same generation of current but its modulation was more delicate and at the higher frequency corresponding to a vocal sound. The electromagnetic device at the other terminal was more sensitive and adapted to follow the finer variations of current.

Radio telegraphy required similar operations. The effect which can cross intervening space is an electromagnetic wave. Radio waves are forced waves following vibrations of electricity just as sound waves follow the vibrations of a musical instrument. A train of waves is produced if there is an oscillation of electricity up and down an antenna wire.

Think of the vertical wire of an antenna system as a tube, or pipe, with walls of negligible thickness and filled with an atmosphere of electrons, discrete and tiny particles of electricity. Deform that evenly spaced atmosphere, produce a crowding of its electrons; and a

vening pages stuck together so that the next page turned would be the first of Chapter 10. That and later chapters can be read without the intervening material, although preferably not; and they contain the ideas most provocative to musicians.

pulse of condensation, like that of a wave in air, will travel along the tube. Reflections will occur at the ends of the tube; and so the pulse will travel up and down until the energy contributed by the original deformation has been dissipated. An analogous action would be that of an organ pipe if it could be excited for only an infinitesimally short time by a single sharp puff of air. Natural vibrations would ensue and gradually damp down. Their frequency would depend upon the time it took for the condensation to travel the length of the pipe.

The electrical vibrations are at high frequency, millions of cycles per second, because the pulse travels up and down the antenna at the enormous speed of light. If a part of the antenna wire is not straight but is spiralled into a coil, that portion acts as if it were a much longer stretch of straight wire. The electrical length of an antenna, therefore, may be effectively increased by inserting a coil of wire—a tuning coil, it is then called, because it alters the effective length and so controls the vibration frequency.

It was the natural vibrations of antennas which were used in the radio of the first decade of this century. In the electrical atmosphere of the antenna a spark set produced a succession of deformations, a few hundred times a second; and each of these resulted in a natural oscillation of more or less rapid death. Such an oscillatory current in an antenna causes the radiation of electromagnetic waves which in turn establish in a distant antenna forced vibrations of similar character. If the receiving antenna is adjusted in effective length so that its own natural period is the same as that of the sending antenna it will respond most efficiently to the force.

The alternations of a current of radio-frequency are too rapid to be heard, even if the diaphragm of a telephone receiver could be made to vibrate at that high rate. The radio current, therefore, must be "detected"; and what is then obtained for the telephone receiver is an envelope, or gross outline, of the variation in current which is occurring in the transmitting antenna. From the spark sets a complex sound was obtained, an inharmonic tone, the fundamental of which had a frequency equal to that of the succession of deformations which excited vibrations in the sending antenna. The sound came in spurts, dash or dot, according to the position of the telegraph key which controlled the spark set.

This sort of a radio telegraph system could not be converted into a radio telephone through replacing its key by a telephone transmitter. The effect which was generated in the antenna had itself certain variations of intensity which would inevitably be presented to a distant listener as a discordant note. In wire telephony the current which is transmitted produces no audible effect except as it is modulated by the vibrations of the transmitter diaphragm. What is required for radio telephony, therefore, is some effect which will be steady and unobtrusive except as controlled by the transmitter. If the oscillations of electricity in a sending antenna can be made uniform—a steady succession of vibrations all of the same amplitude—then there is the possibility of a variation from that uniformity in accordance with spoken word or musical sound.

Several different types of generators for continuous waves were invented during the first few years of this century and by the time the War started a number of them were in use for radio telegraphy. Two of the types were power-driven rotary machines somewhat similar to the standard generators of electrical power. Whatever their design their purpose was to force upon the electronic atmosphere of a sending antenna a steady state of vibration at its own natural frequency.

They found ready acceptance for telegraphy because the start-up-and-die-down characteristic of the waves produced by spark excitation was not adapted to efficient transmission. While the waves were dying out they were likely to be too weak to be observed at a great distance; with the result that most of the time that the sending key was down the receiving station was not getting anything; and the rest of the time what was received was not unlike the static disturbances which the antenna was always picking up.

When continuous waves were broken up into dots and dashes another method of detection was required. The ordinary detector delivered to the receiving operator's headphones a current which followed the gross variation of the radio current in the antenna. If that current was steady there was no variation of the current in the headphones during all the time that the telegraph key was down. There was, it is true, a change of current at the beginning of the telegraph signal and at its conclusion. Corresponding to the first change there would be a single deflection of the receiver diaphragm and to the other a return of the diaphragm to its natural position. But no operator could ever pick out those sounds from the incessant clicks and bangs of static. What static really sounds like is not known to those who listen only to the broadcasting of nearby and high-powered stations—high-powered so as to over-ride static. Try getting a very distant and weak station; and static becomes noticeable or intolerable.

The method of detection which served for spark signals is conveniently called straight detection. The method developed for detecting spurts of continuous waves is that known as heterodyning. With the force of the incoming radio waves is combined another force of the same kind but of a different frequency. At the receiving station there is set up a generator of alternating current of a frequency almost the same as that of the alternating current which is the cause of the continuous waves. The current from the receiving antenna and that from the local generator are both fed to the detector. This device is then subjected to two periodic series of attacks, slightly out of step. The situation of the detector is similar to that of the sidewalk which served at the end of the first chapter in the explanation of beats. Although both the currents are far above any audible frequency they may in this way produce variations, in their net force upon the detector, which are at an audible rate and so will cause a tone in the telephone receiver.

What the telegraph operator heard, therefore, when he got signals from a continuous-wave station by this heterodyne method of beats, was spurts of pure tone with durations corresponding to dots and dashes. The heterodyne generator was the audion which DeForest had invented as a detector. By certain circuit arrangements it was made to serve both purposes at the same time.

Radio telegraphy was well advanced but radio telephony had turned out to be a complete impossibility beyond a few miles. For it there was required the generation of continuous waves, their modulation in conformity with the sounds of speech, transmission of this modulated effect over the desired distance and its demodulation. The sticking point was the amount of modulation which was possible.

Theoretically all that would seem necessary would be to put a carbon-button transmitter in series with the generator which supplies current to the antenna; and so to vary its amount. Unfortunately, to reach any real distance there had to be a large current rushing up and down in the sending antenna. What counted, on the other hand, in radio telephony was the variations in the amount of current. The situation was much like that of a man whom you can hear shouting to you when you can't understand a word he says. It is the variations which carry the information.

In wire telephony this fact had been so completely recognized that no attempt was made to send the total current. Instead there is sent only the equivalent of the variations in the current, as was explained on page 26. In radio telephony, however completely this may have been appreciated, there was in those days no known way of producing more than the feeblest amount of variation in the antenna currents required for great distances.

That was the general state of the radio arts when I first made their acquaintance at the end of 1914 after my part of the work on the transcontinental telephone line was finished. The development of the audion into a dependable high-vacuum tube had provided the amplifier which that line required. But it had other possibilities. Even before that line had been finished some of the research group had been started on the problem of transatlantic and long-distance radio-telephony.

Early in 1915 a field trial was made, one way, from Montauk Point to Wilmington. That summer extensive tests were undertaken from Arlington, Virginia, where the U. S. Navy allowed us the use of its large antenna, beneath which we constructed a small house which we then filled up with vacuum tubes. Engineers with special receiving sets went to Darien, to Mare Island, to Honolulu, and to Paris to receive what was sent from Arlington. We would send a few minutes a day, when the Navy could spare its antenna, and then get cable or wire reports as to what had been heard. Transmission was entirely one way, since the outlying stations were equipped only with receiving sets. In the autumn a real record was established, signalizing the validity of the methods, when in Paris they got a number of words on several occasions.

These experiments developed important principles and early forms of equipment, which after the interruption of the War found application in regular transatlantic service, in broadcasting equipment, in ship-to-shore and in aircraft radio. The fundamental difference between this radio-telephone system and those of earlier attempts lay in the recognition of the possibilities of amplification which the transcontinental line had adumbrated.

Instead of attempting the impracticable task of modulating a large antenna current, from a high-powered generator, completely enough to get its modulations transmitted over large distances the principle of amplification was invoked. There was generated by a vacuum-tube oscillator a small amount of current of the desired radio frequency. Current from a telephone transmitter was caused to modulate this radio-frequency current. This was accomplished by using another vacuum tube and supplying to it both currents under such circuit conditions that the audio-frequency current controlled and varied the intensity of the radio-frequency current.

The result was a small amount of radio current which was practically completely modulated—almost all of it, in other words, had speech significance. Then this current was amplified, actually in two steps by large vacuum tubes, to give it the intensity required for the desired transmission. That principle is still employed; and whether it is a 50-kilowatt broadcasting station or one of the transoceanic telephone stations the formula is: pure ingredients, perfect mixing and amplification to fit the need.

"The atmosphere of sounds in which we live ministers so constantly to our knowledge and enjoyment of our surroundings that through long familiarity we have come to feel, if not contempt, at least indifference toward the marvelous mechanism through which it works. . . . When we hear too faintly or indistinctly we know we need only trace the sound to its source to hear its perfect form, for that is the method we have used from childhood in investigating the sounds of our immediate neighborhood.

"Now with one broad sweep the barriers of time and space are gone and all the world becomes our vocal neighborhood. No longer can we transport ourselves to the origin of a sound, and thus become convinced that we are hearing it aright, for that origin may be thousands of miles away or may have vanished years before; and so we must establish a method to measure the accuracy of the copy which reaches our ears."

These were the opening words of an introduction to a book by Harvey Fletcher, published in 1929, in which were summarized the techniques developed in Bell Laboratories, and the results obtained, in years of investigation of "Speech and Hearing". Although telephone engineers had worked in this field ever since Bell made his first oscillogram of a vowel sound their researches were never carried on very intensively until the development of the vacuum tube made available a most potent tool. The vacuum-tube amplifier permitted investigations with a range and refinement which had been impossible for all earlier students. Speech was the commodity which the telephone industry transported and the human ear was its ultimate consumer and judge. Research, therefore, into the characteristics of speech and the sensitivity of hearing was fundamental to the progress of telephony.

One of the investigations had to do with the operation of the ear as a physical instrument, as a machine for translating sound waves in air into neural stimuli. Measurements were to be made of the least changes in sound which the ear can detect under various conditions of pitch and of acoustic power, and both with and without accompanying noise. The aim was to obtain a quantitative means for comparing individuals in those respects and, from measurements on many persons, to set a standard of average hearing.

The threshold of audibility, that is the minimum intensity a tone can have and just be audible, had been the subject of many earlier investigations. For each pitch what is the minimum of periodically varying air pressure to which the ear will respond with a perception? To determine this a source of sound is needed which can be set for any desired pitch and exactly controlled in its intensity, and for which the amplitude of the air wave can be accurately computed. Telephone receivers had been used for this purpose but their action for such weak sounds was not well enough known to permit accurate computation. They needed investigation as much as did the human ear.

A precision source of sound was required and one was found in the thermophone. This receiver, as its name implies, operates by heating the adjacent air and so causing its expansion. The essential part is a very thin strip of metal—gold foil, for example—through which the current may be sent. The strip is so thin that it heats instantly and, as instantly, communicates its heat to the adjacent air. The amount of heating and the consequent increase of pressure in the air can be calculated in terms of the physical constants of the design and the value of the current. Under proper [1] conditions an alternating current will produce changes in the air pressure which correspond most accurately to the instantaneous variations of the current. As these changes in pressure spread out they constitute a train of air waves with the frequency of the alternating current and with proportional amplitude.

Current of the desired frequency was generated in a vacuum tube arranged as an oscillator; and this current was adjusted, by such a dial control as you probably have on your radio set, until the thermophone produced a just audible tone. The pressure at the ear was then known.

The same device was used also to test electrical ears. With it measurements were made of the response of telephone transmitters to air waves of known ampli-

[1] "Proper" covers a multitude of adjustments and precautions; for example, to obtain proportionality between the variations of air pressure and those of the electrical current, a steady direct current must be superimposed upon the alternating current. All that is physics; which is unnecessary for the general reader. On his behalf the devices mentioned in this book have been drastically simplified. They are always much more complicated even than they appear to be from their descriptions.

tude and power. It, therefore, became possible to set up a system consisting of a transmitter (microphone), which would translate sound waves into electrical current, an amplifier, which would increase the current, a dial-controlled resistance, through which the current could be reduced and so adjusted in value, and a telephone receiver; and to know with exactness just what this system would do to any pure tone. With such a system a wide range of measurements were made on the ear.

In addition to the threshold of audibility there was determined the threshold of feeling. As the pressure of sound upon the ear is increased an intensity is reached for which there is a tickling sensation—or, for very low pitches, a sort of flutter. For still higher intensity there is actual pain. Where pain begins is the upper limit of audibility, the threshold of feeling. Between these thresholds is the range of acoustic pressures for which hearing is possible.

A minimum variation in air pressure is required when the pure tone used for testing lies between 500 and 6000 cycles per second. For that range of frequencies the average ear will respond to a sound wave which can exert upon each square centimeter upon which it falls a pressure between 5 and 10 ten-millionths of that which a gram—a twenty-eighth of an ounce— would exert by its weight. The most severe alternating pressure which the ear can stand without pain is as much as one or two grams weight if the frequency is in the range 200 to 1500 cycles. At about 1000 cycles the ear can handle the greatest range of pressures. For frequencies lower, or higher, the range is much reduced; a greater variation is required to produce an audible sensation and a smaller pressure will cause pain. At the high frequency of approximately 20,000 cycles the thresholds meet; and similarly for the low of about 16. These frequencies mark the upper and lower frequency limits of audibility.

What the thresholds of audibility and of feeling delimit is more realistically expressed in terms of power. In ordinary daily life we usually meet the word "power" in only two situations: the rating of an automobile in conventional horsepower and the rating of electric lamp-bulbs in watts. In neither case are we likely to have any muscular conception of what is meant. Instead of attempting to clarify either of these two ideas it is easier to introduce a third situation and state its corresponding power.

The average power involved in speech was measured for a number of different persons while they were talking in their usual conversational manner. Strictly speaking, what was determined was the pressure of a sound wave of speech at some measured distance from the mouth of a speaker. Right in front of the mouth, where the power starts to spread out, the air molecules in their vibration have an amplitude of only six or seven thousandths, or so, of a millimeter—not over three ten-thousandths of an inch. Obviously the measurement of such a delicate variation in pressure is a refined operation. It was accomplished by the use of a calibrated electrical ear, that is, a telephone transmitter the response of which to sound waves was accurately known from tests in which it had been exposed to known sounds from a thermophone.

From measurements of the variation of pressure which a speech wave produces in the air through which it travels, it is possible, knowing physics and applying a little mathematics, to calculate the total power emerging from its source. Ten millionths of a watt, that is, 10 microwatts, was found to be about the average power which radiates from the mouth of a speaker. Without attempting to measure the size of the mouth, it is a fair approximation to think of this power, as it starts to spread, as evenly distributed over an imaginary surface, cupped closely around the mouth, which has an area of ten square centimeters. Through each square centimeter there flows one microwatt of acoustic power. One would have to talk continuously for more than a hundred thousand successive days to radiate as much energy as does a 25-watt lamp in an hour.

This acoustic power level of one microwatt, per square centimeter of area across its path, is a convenient reference level from which other levels may be scaled in terms of decibels. It is the reference against which are plotted the thresholds of audibility and of feeling in the chart on page 230.

The determination of these thresholds involved a number of consequences. Instruments of remarkable precision had been required in the conduct of the investigation; one of these was the thermophone and the other a most accurate electrical ear, the condenser transmitter. This device consists in essence of two parallel metal plates, one fixed and the other a movable stretched diaphragm. They are electrically insulated from each other and separated by about a thousandth of an inch of air. When a sound wave vibrates the diaphragm its motion is not only microscopic but highly damped—the thin layer of air acts like a cushion to prevent any natural vibration. The damping helps to make the instrument practically distortionless in its translation of wave motion into current.

The translation is the result of the action of the two plates as an electrical condenser. For operation the terminals of a battery are connected to the plates. In that instant a tiny current flows and charges them electrically, giving to the one which is connected to the negative terminal an extra number of electrons and withdrawing from the other an equal number. The plates will remain in that charged state, and no more current will flow, as long as the battery is connected, provided only that the separation of the plates is not altered. The reason for this provision is that the amount of current, the number of electrons which must flow in order to charge the plates, depends upon their separation. If they are closer it takes more current to charge them; if farther apart, less. The plates constitute an electrical condenser; and its capacity for holding electricity is greater, ceteris paribus, the nearer they are together.

As the diaphragm vibrates the separation changes periodically. When it becomes less more electrons can be accommodated and a small additional current flows instantly, taking for its trip from battery to plate about as little time as would a beam of light following the same path. When the separation is increased fewer electrons can be held and the excess return to their former places. The current from the battery to the plates, therefore, follows with complete fidelity and amazing promptness each minute displacement of the diaphragm.

It follows accurately but is too small to be of any practical value until it is highly amplified. For that reason a vacuum-tube amplifier is always associated with this transmitter; and very closely, because the feeble current must be amplified before it travels more than a few feet lest it be obscured by accidental but larger currents which might be induced by neighboring electrical currents.

This transmitter, which was developed [1] primarily as a laboratory instrument in an investigation of speech and hearing, picked up such a wide range of frequencies and intensities that it was not long, on a research timetable, before it became the famous "mike" of radio broadcasting and the first sound pictures. It is only one, however, of modern instances of research developments turned practical. Through its use, combined with the vacuum-tube amplifier and other telephonic developments including receivers which can reproduce a wide range of frequencies and intensities, investigations of speech, music and hearing have proceeded, both within and without Bell Laboratories, at a rapid acceleration.

For some of the studies the condenser transmitter was not required, but high-quality receivers were and also occasionally the more powerful ones known as loudspeakers. One of these investigations, and the next logically after blocking out by thresholds the hearing range of the ear, is that of its differential perception.

What is the ability of the ear to distinguish between

[1] Cf. "Signals and Speech", Chapter 9.

successive sounds in the matter of pitch? What is the minimum perceptible difference? This is not primarily to be measured by the mere difference in frequency of two successive pure tones between which the ear can just discriminate. Instead it is to be treated as a musical interval and determined by the ratio of the frequencies of the two tones. The musical interval, for example, represented by a "major tone", ratio 9/8, corresponds to a difference in frequency of 32 cycles if the keynote is middle C (256) but to 48 if it is the G (384), a fifth above. Although the actual number of cycles depends upon the pitch chosen as the keynote, the ratio corresponding to the interval is the same under all conditions. It is independent of pitch. The minimum perceptible interval, on the other hand, is not a constant. It is some complicated function not only of pitch but also of the intensity of the two tones which are being compared.

Tests have been carried out by listening over and over again, but alternately, to two similar tones, one fixed and the other adjustable in frequency, while the interval between them was decreased until it ceased to be perceived as existent, or increased until it was just noticeable. The tones arose from two vacuum-tube oscillators and were heard through head phones. If the switch from one sound to the other takes place two or three times a second the ear is capable of its greatest discrimination. The two tones which are to be compared must, of course, be pure sinusoidal vibrations and offer no basis for differentiation except their pitches.

At first thought it would appear that they would

meet this condition of equality, except in pitch, if they were adjusted to be of the same acoustical power. Sounds so adjusted are not at equal levels above the threshold of audibility, nor are they equally loud in the judgment of the ear. Since tests under any single one of the three conditions, namely, equal power, equal loudness, and equal levels above threshold, would not be conclusive it is necessary to map out the entire hearing area. Tests have been made, starting with tones of frequency 31, 62, 125, 250 and so on by octaves to 8000 and then to 11,700, approximately the fifth higher. For each frequency the tests were repeated for a number of different conditions of power, starting 5 db above the threshold level and continuing with steps first of 5 and then of 10 db. The results are on page 231.

A typical observation is that for a tone of 1000 cycles per second at a level of 60 db above that at which the tone was just audible to the observers. A tone similar thereto, except in frequency, can just be recognized as different if it is separated by the interval 1.0022/1, that is, if it is 0.22 of one percent higher, or lower, in frequency. For this same frequency of 1000 cycles but at progressively lower power levels the perceptible interval is increasingly greater, reaching at 5 db above the threshold the value of 1.0094/1, corresponding to 0.94 percent.

Comparing what the ear can do at different pitches for tones which are at the same intensity level, it appears that its behavior is quantitatively different for low and for high frequencies. Above 500 cycles the minimum perceptible interval is approximately constant. The actual number of cycles, therefore, by which two just distinguishable pure tones will differ is greater at the higher frequencies. On the other hand, below about 500 cycles the ear seems able to discriminate between two frequencies to about three cycles regardless of the pitch. This difference in actual cycles being approximately constant means that the ear requires an interval which is greater the lower the pitch.

The data cited above were obtained by listening monaurally through a telephone receiver. Supplementary tests showed that two ears were somewhat more sensitive to pitch differences than either ear alone. The percentages are perhaps only two thirds as large. Intermediate between the monaural and the binaural sensitivities are those for bone conduction where a special design of receiver is placed against the mastoid process.

From a musical standpoint these results are of interest as indicating about the limits of the ear's ability to judge whether successive pure tones are identical in pitch or not. According to the tests, for example, it is almost impossible to distinguish between two pure tones, one of frequency 62 cycles per second and the other of 65 cycles. The musician,[1] however, deals with complex not pure tones. His judgment of similarity in pitch can depend not only upon the fundamental but also upon the overtones. For these two notes the seventh overtones would be 496 and 520 cycles. Im-

[1] Normal ears apparently differ less than the brains with which they are associated. In the matter of minimum perceptible increment the ear of the musician, or student, is no more capable than that of the musically untrained. The judgment of the musician, however, as to what are the pitches of the notes will be the more accurate. The sense of "absolute pitch" is a remarkable ability.

agine that he heard only those overtones; he would have no difficulty in recognizing that their pitches differed. Even if they were very faint he could recognize an interval as small as that between 496 and 504 cycles. In so far, therefore, as overtones enter into his sensations his accuracy is not limited by the minimum perceptible interval which applies to pure tones of the fundamental pitch.

When notes are complex their overtones permit a listener to distinguish smaller differences in pitch on the part of the fundamentals than would be recognizable from the fundamentals alone. This is in part for the reason which has just been illustrated numerically and in part, probably, because each overtone adds to the data on which judgment is based. Of course, this violates the condition previously stated for the determination of the minimum perceptible increment of pitch. In determining that characteristic of the ear there must be no basis for differentiation except pitch. Except under laboratory conditions, such as those under which the data cited above were obtained, there is almost always some basis besides pitch.

The musician, because of that fact, is rarely limited in judging pitch by the inherent ability of his ear. His music is produced and heard in auditoriums, private houses, and partially enclosed spaces like stadia. Music reaches the ear simultaneously by many different paths and after many reflections from walls and ceiling. Each pure tone undergoes a different series of reflections, absorptions and interferences as is discussed more fully in the chapter on Auditorium Acoustics. The interference patterns which the sound sources establish differ so greatly with pitch and with the position of the listening ear that changes in pitch as small as 0.01 of one percent can be detected in the range from 3000 to 10,000 cycles. Tests of this kind are usually carried out by listening to a loudspeaker which produces a pure tone that swings up and down in pitch three or four times a second. If the test were made in a wide out-of-door space the discrimination would be practically the same as for the head receiver test and much less keen than for a closed space.

Of almost as much importance, as its ability to discriminate between tones of different pitch, is the ear's minimum perceptible increment of intensity. If two pure tones of the same pitch but at different levels of acoustic power are sounded successively the ear cannot detect a difference when the power levels do not differ by more than some minimum. If the Weber-Fechner law, previously mentioned, held accurately for hearing this limit would be the same for all levels of power. Actually it is not; and it must always be expressed as the number of decibels by which the power level of a pure tone of stated frequency must be increased or decreased from a stated level in order that it shall be perceptibly different.

For frequencies in the approximate range 300 to 4000 cycles the value of the minimum varies from about 0.25 db for levels near the threshold of feeling to two or even three decibels near that of audibility. For higher or lower frequencies the values are considerably larger. At the best, a pure tone with an acoustic power of one microwatt (per sq. cm.) can be distinguished from a similar and succeeding tone of power

1.06 microwatts—a difference of six percent. In the ranges of frequencies and of power levels to which the ear is usually subjected, by ordinary speech and by most music, its average value is approximately one-third decibel or ten percent. The data are presented on page 232.

The sounds of everyday life are not pure; thresholds and minimum perceptible increments, therefore, are only the beginning of knowledge about the behavior of the ear. How accurately it will recognize complex sounds, particularly those of speech; how much of musical sound it can perceive; how far its interpretation of pitch differs from the physical fact of vibration frequency and under what conditions; what subjective interpretations it may give to complex sounds; how noise may mask the sounds it would hear and effectively raise its threshold of hearing; and how it relates loudness and acoustic power; all these questions are the subject of present scientific interest. Some of the answers will be presented in later chapters.

6 TRANSLATION AND TRANSMISSION

When the drummer tunes his instrument he does so by adjusting the tension of its membrane. More tightly stretched, the natural rate of vibration is higher and the pitch correspondingly higher. That is equally true of the diaphragms of transmitters and microphones.

In telephone transmitters of early vintage the natural frequency of the diaphragm was well in the middle of the voice range. Since a vibrating system responds most completely to forced vibrations when they are of its own natural frequency, this was an advantage in the days before vacuum-tube amplifiers because the diaphragm would vibrate with greater amplitude and consequently produce larger variations in current. It generated a larger amount of speech-bearing alternating current and hence there was more to be received at the distant terminal. The disadvantage was the unfair discrimination, which was quite severe, against frequencies in the voice which differed very much from the natural frequency. Such transmitters served for the transmission of information although they did not transmit faithfully as wide a range of pure tones as enter into speech. They did not approach in quality the condenser transmitter which made radio broadcasting and sound pictures esthetic media.

To obtain more uniform response to sound waves of different frequencies it was necessary to tighten the diaphragm until its natural frequency was as high as practicable, above as many of the tones of speech and of music as was possible. For frequencies well below its own the diaphragm would then respond practically without unfairness; but only grudgingly. The resultant vibration, although following with fidelity the force of a complex sound wave, had no vigor. It was a faint hearted and unnatural response and could only be made effective through the cooperation of the vacuum-tube amplifier. By sacrificing momentarily magnitude of response, fidelity of translation was obtained. The condenser transmitter produces a current variation which is proportional to the driving force of the sound wave for a wide range of frequencies. Its natural vibrations are moved up in frequency to a point where they are less important.

Natural vibrations, however, ensue whenever a vibrating system undergoes a deformation and thereafter is allowed unchecked to restore its own equilibrium. The first push that is given to it establishes such oscillations. The moment it is free, it adopts its own method of coming back to rest. If that were not so there would be none of the usual musical instruments for their sounds are entirely formed by natural oscillations.

Imagine, for example, what happens when a sound wave, involving a single sinusoidal component, impinges upon an elastic membrane. It starts to drive the membrane according to its own notions. To its first imposition there is a transient objection, a struggle to return from the displacement in a natural manner. This transient merely subtracts from the imposed vibration, less and less as the latter continues, until a steady responsive state is reached where the membrane follows its master submissively. When, however, the sound ceases, and its urge no longer controls, then things revert to their primitive state and the natural vibrations have the last word. A faint "-ing" of sound follows the termination of the forced vibration.

If the membrane is that of a transmitter this final gasp will be converted into current variations and, as such, pursue its way to the distant receiver where it will be reproduced. That should not be allowed to occur if translation is not to be marred by glosses and perversions introduced by the translator. The solution is to damp out the natural vibration. Rubber pads were used in early days but with the advent of the condenser transmitter air damping was seen to be a very satisfactory method. The diaphragm vibrates against a cushion of air; for which there are provided small escape openings. The action is somewhat like that of the pistons which are used as door checks to prevent slamming.

There are some nice equations which state for a vibrating system the relationships of its physical magnitudes: elasticity or stiffness, mass or inertia, and resistance. The natural frequency is determined by the first two of these quantities. The resistance, which includes frictional and submolecular resistances, determines the rate at which energy is used up in work or dissipated in heat. As the energy available for a natural vibration is used up the amplitude of vibration dies down. How rapidly it damps out depends upon the resistance which is met and the mass which must be moved. If the mass of the vibrating body is large its damping is slower because its greater inertia tends to carry it past its normal position of rest. Small mass for vibrating parts and large resistance are requirements in the design of translating devices whether transmitters or receivers. In a recent model of a high-power loud speaker, one which will radiate into the air as much as 500 watts— *not* microwatts—the diaphragm is a thin tensioned sheet of duralumin, only 0.01 of an inch in thickness.

The mathematically expressed relationships for vibrating systems of ponderable matter are identical in form with those for vibrations of electricity in conducting systems. Corresponding to each physical magnitude of one set of equations there is an analogue in the other. Resistance in both is the cause for the dissipation of energy. Stiffness in one corresponds to electrical capacity in the other; mass, or inertia, corresponds to the electrical quantity known as inductance—the characteristic of conducting paths which spiral or coil. In the antenna system which was described on page 48 the addition of a coil changes the natural frequency, because it changes the electrical mass of the system while there remains unchanged the electrical capacity which it possesses because the vertical wire and the ground act like the two plates of a condenser.

This similarity of relationships between electrical and mechanical vibrations is of more than academic importance. It has been one of the fruitful points of view in the telephonic arts. In the early part of the century engineers reasoned about electrical systems by analogy with the better known mechanical systems. They explained the transmission characteristic of a loaded telephone line by analogy with a vibrating string which is strung with beads to increase its mass just as the electrical line has coils to increase its inductance. Very soon, however, the shoe was on the other foot. Methods, both of mathematical analysis and of design, which had been developed for electrical circuits and their vibrations or wave motions, came to be applied to mechanical problems. The electrical arts had progressed so rapidly and so far that the stream of analogies and techniques could run the other way. Two illustrations, one of a vibrating system for phonographs and the other of an acoustical filter, are of very practical importance but too technical for present description.

Both electrical and mechanical systems are involved in telephony. At the terminals the transmitter and receiver are electro-mechanical systems for converting wave trains in air into waves in the electronic atmosphere of the intervening line, and vice versa. The lines are electrical systems which have transmission characteristics dependent upon their construction. Over the New York-Denver line, for example, as it opened in 1911, it was assumed, in the absence of the more reliable apparatus for measurements which vacuum tubes soon made possible, that there would be transmitted without discrimination all those components of speech with frequencies between about 100 cycles and 2100 cycles. To have built that line to transmit higher frequencies would have resulted in a much more expensive structure, necessarily higher toll charges for its use and better quality than then appeared necessary for the ordinary purposes of business communication. Actually, as later measurements showed, frequencies as low as 1800 were seriously discriminated against. Today whether one telephones within his own city or across as many state boundaries as possible he is talking probably over a line which transmits a full thousand cycles more.

When one listens to a radio broadcast what frequencies he may perceive depends upon his receiver and upon the station to which it is tuned. But between the studio and that station, and in fact all the others of the network, the speech and music travel over special telephone lines, called "program circuits", which will carry with practically equal efficiency all the frequencies from 100 to 5000 cycles per second.

Even wider frequency ranges have been transmitted for experimental and demonstration purposes. In April of 1933 a concert by the Philadelphia Orchestra was picked up by transmitters in its Academy of Music, transmitted by special telephone circuits to Washington and there reproduced in Constitution Hall. The telephone line had a transmission characteristic flat to within one decibel between 40 and 15,000 cycles. Three parallel lines were used and their characteristics are shown on page 234. In the Academy there were three microphones, to each of which was assigned one of these circuits. They terminated in Constitution Hall in three loudspeakers. The positions of the microphones and the corresponding positions of the loudspeakers were so arranged that the music was reproduced in auditory perspective, essentially as it was heard in the original auditorium. This demonstration, which was attended by a large public audience including many experts in music, proved conclusively that electrical facilities are available for complete and faithful transmission and reproduction of the output of a full-sized orchestra.

As to the musical and acoustical aspects of that achievement more will be said in later chapters. For the present there will be described some of the techniques and equipment which made it possible.

As translating devices there were employed new designs of microphones and loudspeakers. The former were of the moving-coil type in which the diaphragm carries a coil of wire. As the coil vibrates it changes its position in a fairly intense magnetic field and therefore has induced in it a current proportional to its motion. The action is similar to that of an ordinary generator in a power plant except that there the motion is one of continuous revolution instead of complex vibration. The devices are unusually efficient as translators; for example, when actuated by a 1000-cycle sound wave with an intensity of one microwatt (per square centimeter) they will deliver 0.05 microwatt of electrical power to the transmission line. They will respond to frequencies over the entire range from 40 to 15,000 cycles but have a peculiar dependence upon the angle which their diaphragms present to the sound waves. They are most sensitive, as one would expect, when the wave strikes a full instead of a glancing blow, and as they were used this was generally the situation. The response-frequency characteristic appears on page 235.

The loudspeakers were formed by two units, each a moving coil device, one designed to receive the currents of low frequency and the other those of higher frequency. The high-frequency unit is a multiple composed of sixteen horns pointed to cover a wide area, because high-frequency sound waves are more directional than low and a single horn can reach only those auditors who happen to be in the essentially conical pathway of its sound.

The response-frequency characteristic of a receiver is not a physical characteristic which is independent of its situation. In a small room, where there will be numerous reflections from walls and ceiling, a loudspeaker's behavior is very different from that in a large room or in the free space of out-of-doors. In a large hall the combined units of these loudspeakers give a response which is flat within about plus or minus 4 db between 40 and 5000 cycles. Above 5000 the response diminishes rapidly for higher and higher frequencies up to its limit of about 15,000 cycles. At that point it is about 25 db less responsive than at 5000 cycles. In the overall effect this "drooping" characteristic did not matter, as much as it might have, because it was partly compensated by a rising characteristic in the microphones. The microphones, in other words, outdid themselves for the highest frequencies and so the team of microphone and loudspeaker handled all frequencies more nearly alike.

The overall transmission characteristic (shown on page 236), despite this approximate compensation, was not as flat as was desired. There was, therefore, introduced into the transmission circuit, which connected the translating mechanisms, an electrical network which would distort the transmission in such a way that the overall effect of the entire system would be faithful pickup and reproduction. Such a network is known to its designers as an "equalizer". It is formed by an arrangement of coils and condensers which is calculated to produce minimum transmission losses for alternating currents in some ranges of frequency and for other ranges losses as desired. These networks were designed after measurements had been made of the output of the loudspeakers in their final positions in Constitution Hall. The measurements provided data as to how adequately the loudspeakers would cover the audience and allowed a design of network which insured an essentially flat frequency characteristic for the whole system between orchestra in Philadelphia and audience in Washington.

After practically perfect transmission had been secured there were inserted into the circuit several other networks, similar in general principle to the equalizer, but intended to permit a controllable distortion at the will of the musical director. Through their levers they allowed certain ranges of frequencies to be degraded or enhanced. When, for example, in the judgment of the director components of sound with frequencies below 1000 cycles should be made more powerful a network could be cut in which would produce a progressively greater effect at lower frequencies, amounting to 5 db at 30 cycles. Meanwhile the components of frequency above 1000 would be unaffected unless one of the other networks were thrown into the circuit. In the extreme case, as shown on page 238, it was possible to reduce the efficiency of the system so that components above 1000 cycles suffered in proportion to their frequencies, with the 15,000 cycle component down about 28 db from its physically, if not musically, correct level of intensity.

The entire system from the acoustical standpoint included: two halls, the acoustics of which were known and allowed for in the placement of microphones and loudspeakers; a practically perfect transmission line with telephone repeaters along its route; equalizing networks; amplifiers; and special networks for control which allowed new possibilities in the creation or interpretation of orchestral music. The system had also to meet certain situations as to the acoustic power which it was to pick-up and others as to that which it was to deliver. These situations are determined by auditorium acoustics, by noise and its masking effect and by the physical facts as to the power output of musical instruments, solo and ensemble. These subjects await the reader in later chapters.

The transmission circuit itself, however, deserves some present attention, in part because it represents a distinct advance in the art and in part because it exemplifies most conveniently the main operations which must be performed in any electrical transmission whether by wire or by radio.

In any communication system the character of the terminal apparatus, that is of the translating mechanisms, depends upon the type of signals in the code of which the message is expressed. If the code is one of audible signals, speech or music, then one mechanism must be sound-sensitive and its complimentary partner an electrically controlled source of sound. If the information is to be in the form of typewritten characters one translator must be responsive to a keyboard and the other must control a printing mechanism. If picture, or scene, is to be sent the terminal equipments are

respectively light-sensitive and light-active. In all cases
the first translator produces a current with variations
characteristic of the effects imposed upon it; and the
second, when supplied with that current, or with a
current equivalent in character, recreates the original
effects for eye or ear. It is immaterial so far as the action
of the second translator is concerned whether it receives
the original current of the first or "something just as
good"; nor is it material through what medium or
route this something may travel provided only no
salient variation is lost in transmission.

Only in the simplest cases, or for the shortest distances, is the actual current of the transmitter sent to
the receiver. For the longer distances, the transmitter
current may be caused to modulate some other current,
or electrical effect, which is better adapted to the route
between sender and receiver. This current, or effect,
then becomes the carrier of the information.

In the generalized case, a microphone, M, delivers
its audio-frequency current to a transmitting station, T.
At T a generator produces an alternating current of
an ultra-audible frequency. This "carrier-frequency"
current meets the audio-frequency current in a "modulator", usually a properly conditioned vacuum tube. In
effect what there takes place is a marriage of the
currents and the production of twin offspring,[1] alternating currents, one of which has a frequency the sum
of those of its parents and the other a frequency which
is the difference of the parental frequencies. At this
point, in the usual situation, the father dies or is electrically divorced. There then leaves station, T, the

[1] Cf. Chapter 5, "Signals and Speech".

carrier current, or mother, and her two sideband children, each of whom resembles her while retaining full hereditary record of its paternity. These three alternating currents then proceed to the receiving station, R, where they are "demodulated", usually in a properly conditioned vacuum tube. Within that tube, by processes which need not be detailed, there is born an audio-frequency current that is the living image of the late-departed father. This audio current then travels to the loudspeaker, L.

If between stations T and R there are no guiding wires the currents which leave the modulator pass through a powerful amplifier and go climb an antenna. As they surge up and down this structure they radiate effects which give rise in distant antennas, of the same tune, to minute but similar currents. It is these currents which enter the demodulator at station R. If wires are used between these stations the currents proceed directly to the demodulator, undergoing en route such amplification as may be necessary to offset attenuation. The only essential differences between the two types of transmission media are: first, that the carrier current is of enormously high frequency in radio but in wire systems usually [1] between 20,000 and 100,000 cycles; second, that the amplification must be much higher in radio; and third, that the message is broadcast instead of being privately delivered to a single receiver.

[1] Usually as of today but perhaps not as of tomorrow. A "coaxial" or concentric cable has been developed in the Bell Laboratories which will transmit a band one or two million cycles wide. It can carry 240 simultaneous telephone conversations each on a carrier current of distinctive frequency. In effect the cable provides between its terminals a small but adequate tube of "ether" along which private messages may be guided without mutual interference.

For the transmission of the orchestral concert from Philadelphia to Washington the carrier current was a pure sinusoid of 40,000 cycles per second. If in the audio-frequency current from the microphone there was a component of 1500 cycles then the current which emerged from the modulator had three components, one the carrier current, one of frequency 40,000 + 1500 = 41,500, and the other of frequency 40,000 — 1500 = 38,500. The amplitudes of these sideband currents were proportional at each instant to the amplitude of the 1500-cycle current. Similar arithmetic holds for all the other possible frequencies in the microphone current; with the result that there issued from the modulator two sidebands of current, one with frequencies 25,000 to 40,000 and the other 40,000 to 55,000.

In radio transmission both sidebands are radiated. In most carrier-current telephone systems only one is transmitted, since either contains all the necessary variations. The upper band was therefore eliminated by an "electrical filter", a complex network which is in effect a short artificial telephone line designed to pass a certain band of frequencies and to discriminate destructively against all other frequencies. As a matter of fact it is also unnecessary to transmit the carrier itself, provided that an identical current can be generated at the receiving station to mate with the sideband in the demodulator. Its transmission means just that extra amount of current which may overload the amplifiers along the route. In the Philadelphia-Washington circuit the carrier also was cut out by a filter; and only the band carrying the music was transmitted.

To provide at Washington a current equivalent to

the suppressed carrier there was sent a small current of 20,000 cycles, a value well outside the frequencies important to the reproduction of the music. At the Washington station this 20,000 cycle current passed through an electrical system which doubled its frequency. The resulting current of 40,000 cycles was then used in the operation of demodulation to obtain currents of frequencies 0-15,000, corresponding to what the microphones heard at Philadelphia.

The electrical operations involved in this telephonic transmission are typical of the most general case.

7 LOUDNESS

Things equal to the same thing are, axiomatically, equal to each other, according to Euclid and the consensus since his time. Is the proposition true for sensations? If, for example, a, b, and c are three pure tones of different frequencies and if a and b appear to the ear as of equal loudness and similarly b and c; then will a and c sound equally loud? The answer, that they will, was obtained years ago in an investigation of "the loudness of pure tones".

Human ears, which have on the average equal thresholds of audibility, will have on the average—and "on the average" must always be said or understood because ears do differ—the same ability to detect a difference in power level between two pure tones which are otherwise identical. When the ear detects such a difference it ascribes to the tones an inequality in loudness. At the frequency of 1300 cycles per second there can be distinguished about 370 successive levels between the thresholds of audibility and of feeling. The steps between levels are not of equal size in decibels but are larger near the auditory threshold, as was explained in the chapter on Researches in Audition.

When a comparison of loudness is to be made between tones of different frequencies the Euclidean postulate is useful. A reference tone is selected as a standard of loudness against which all other tones, of whatever audible and tolerable intensities, may be compared. In some of the earlier work a pure tone of 700 cycles was used but today the accepted standard is one of 1000 cycles.

In one of the investigations each observer was first carefully and repeatedly tested to find for this standard frequency the power level which represented his auditory threshold. The tone was derived from a matched pair of telephone receivers which were supplied through an adjustable attenuating network by the amplified current from a vacuum-tube oscillator. The power level of the 1000-cycle tone was then set some distance, expressed in decibels, above this just audible level. Another similar circuit, but one supplying a different frequency of current, could be switched to the receivers. The observer listened to their sounds alternately; adjusting the power of the second until it appeared of equal loudness with the first. When that level had been determined with the greatest practicable precision the second oscillator was altered in frequency and the procedure was repeated to determine another condition of equality. In this way there were found for a wide range of frequencies the power levels which produced sensations of loudness equal, according to the ears and judgment of each observer, to the sensation of a chosen power level of the 1000-cycle tone.

It was next necessary to adopt some scale for the expression of these results. It was decided to define the "loudness level" of any tone by the statement of the power level of the 1000-cycle reference tone of equal loudness. About this time there came into common use, also, a new reference level for intensity. Instead of starting the zero for the decibel scale at the power level of one microwatt, which was discussed in the chapter on Scales, a much lower level was adopted. A power one ten-thousand-millionth as large was chosen; that is, a level 100 db lower. The new level is therefore that of a ten-thousand-million-millionth of a watt (per square centimeter in a plane free wave).

There are a number of reasons why this intensity level is preferred by acoustical experts; and one of these is important to the lay reader. It is roughly that of the threshold of audibility for tones in the important middle range of audible frequencies, those between 500 and 2500 cycles per second. The latest determinations of thresholds, and their relationship to this level of 1/10,000,000,000,000,000th of a watt, are shown in the chart of page 239.

Measuring power from this level, which is conveniently written as 10^{-16} watt, means expressing intensities by the number of decibels above—or below, for that matter—the just audible power of a 1000-cycle pure tone. This is convenient to otologists and psychologists who are accustomed to scale upward from the lower threshold, sometimes using the term "sensation unit" instead of decibel to describe any higher level. It should be and is, or probably will be, convenient to the musician for it gives him a reference which he can relate to his own experience—the intensity of a note two octaves above middle C when he can just hear it. For each ten-fold increase of power above that level the intensity is ten decibels higher.

The 1000-cycle tone is a possible standard against which to compare the loudness of other tones because experiment has shown that loudness levels are "things" within the meaning of the Euclidean postulate. Comparisons have been made which map out contours of equal loudness within the range of hearing. Any contour is described as a "loudness level" and its numerical value is the number of decibels that the reference tone is above zero level. For the middle range of frequencies, between 700 and 4000 cycles, tones of equal loudness are also of practically equal intensity. At a lower frequency a tone must be many times as intense to sound equally loud. On the other hand, as is pictured in the chart on page 240, for tones of low frequency a smaller increase in intensity is required to produce a sensation of increased loudness.

If one listens to music a hundred feet away from its source and then approaches to a point only ten feet away the intensity level for all its sounds will be raised at his ear by 20 db. All the tones below 700 cycles will sound disproportionately louder. If in the distant music a 100-cycle and a 1200-cycle tone were equally loud, then, at the shorter distance the 100-cycle tone will have a loudness level almost 20 db above the higher pitched tone. For higher frequencies the effect is less; but for still lower frequencies it is even more pronounced. The converse of this phenomenon is the marked decrease in loudness of low tones as music becomes more distant. A radio loudspeaker heard across a city street does not sound as it does to those in the same room with it. Its bass, if it really has any to start with, is probably near the loudness level of zero.

"Loudness" is a psychological term which has as yet no commonly accepted equivalent in physical terms.

This difficulty has been dodged by the use of the concept "loudness level". To this there is a definite physical value—the intensity level of the equally loud reference tone as expressed in decibels above the reference intensity. Although this method of comparing the loudness characteristics of sounds has technical advantage it is not ordinarily satisfying to one whose interest is primarily esthetic. It is technical in language and in concept; and it demands keeping constantly in mind the meaning of the decibel scale—or reviewing it.

About all that needs to be remembered, however, is this: power doubles for three decibels, quadruples for six, and is increased ten-fold for every ten. Thirty decibels up, for example, means an increase in power of 1000 times; and thirty down a decrease to one one-thousandth. Thirty-six decibels would mean 1000 x 4 or four thousand times. A decrease of 23 decibels would mean a reduction to 1/200th.

If the 1000-cycle reference tone is raised 3 db its power is doubled. When that must be done to meet a change in loudness of some other tone which is under comparison, it means that the power of the second tone has been increased between 1.4 and 2.0 times depending upon its frequency. That is the ratio for frequencies up to 700 cycles; between that frequency and 5000 cycles the ratio is practically constant at 2.0 and above 5000 it is slightly less than two.

Doubling the power of a tone is not doubling its loudness. On the other hand is there any exact significance to such a popular estimate of loudness as "twice as loud"? Is there any quantity which is the physical essence of loudness such that if it is doubled the loudness is doubled? The question is one to which psychologists and students of acoustics have frequently attempted to obtain a satisfactory answer. For a while during the investigations of recent years it looked as if an answer would be obtained in terms of minimum audible increments of intensity. Between the thresholds there are for each frequency fairly definite numbers of perceptibly different levels of intensity. It was suggested that the mind dealt in terms of those increments. A sound the intensity of which was $2n$ steps above the threshold would be twice as loud as one which was only n steps above. Unfortunately this simple theory failed to meet the test of all the facts. Sounds which are equal numbers of perceptible steps above their thresholds are not equally loud.

In the meantime psychologists and others pursued their investigations into what an average auditor meant when he said a sound was half or twice as loud. If one's ears are equally normal he might expect to hear a sound with only half its loudness when he completely shielded one ear. Using only one ear there would then reach the brain only half as many "nerve discharges"; and if the magnitude of the sensation depends upon the number which arrives the loudness would be halved. Starting from such a basis of experience an observer might be expected to make a more or less reliable estimate.

Many students of acoustics are coming to believe that a scale based on such estimates is psychologically justifiable and would be of practical usefulness. It would have the advantage of a certain naturalness and would avoid the necessity of conditioning observers of sounds by training and association processes. For small differences in loudness it would be a convenience but probably for general use the decibel scale is to be preferred. Experts in electrical communication who have trained themselves to associate sound intensities with the decibel scale, in which their adjusting dials are usually calibrated, are surprisingly accurate in their estimates and judgments. Perhaps the answer is to equip schools of music with thousand-cycle sources, loudspeakers, and intervening attenuators which permit changing the power level by specified numbers of decibels. In some such way the musical youth of the country might come to a common language, or at least dialect, for the discussion of loudness.

The musician's interest is not in the loudness of pure tones for he practically never deals with them except to such approximations as stopped organ pipes may represent. To the physicist and psychologist the loudness sensations for pure tones are the necessary basis for any consideration of the loudness of complex sounds whether of music, speech or noise. The experimental determination of the loudness level of a complex sound is easily accomplished by comparison with the 1000-cycle reference tone. Its intensity level is the loudness level of any complex sound which is equally loud. For any sound, which can be repeated at will, there may thus be determined the relationship between intensity and loudness level.

Such practical information, however, is not enough for the scientist. He wishes to know to what extent and why each overtone or component in the complex contributes to the loudness level; and thus to be able to calculate and predict, from a knowledge of the over-tone structure of a note and its intensity, what its loudness will be. In arriving at an adequate formula he wishes to obtain at the same time explanations for the actions of inner ear and nerves through which power levels of components are translated into perceptions of loudness. The theories of physical and physiological action which he develops and upon which he bases his formulas must explain not only the known facts of loudness, and any new ones which experiment may disclose, but also all the other data as to the ear including thresholds and minimum perceptible differences which have been discussed in earlier chapters and several important phenomena which will appear later.

According to the indications, from the best researches so far published, the formulas and the theory when finally completed will involve respectively too many terms and related facts for any except the special student. The lay reader will probably have to accept the results without the theory or method of derivation. Some experimental data, however, are available on the loudness of complex tones in terms of their overtone structures.

A simple or pure tone is described by its frequency and intensity. For a complex sound there is required a similar description for each of its components. An alternative description adapted to musical notes with their harmonic overtones is a statement for each musical instrument of the typical structure of its notes. Each component is described by stating the multiple which its frequency is of the fundamental frequency and the fraction which its intensity is of the intensity of the fundamental. For the G string of a violin, for example, the frequencies starting with the fundamental are as: 1, 2, 3, 4, 5, 6; and in the same way the intensities are as: 1; 0.2; 0.02; 0.003; 0.01; 0.003. If these intensities are expressed in decibels above the intensity of the fundamental pure tone the descriptive series becomes: 0; − 7; − 17; − 25; − 20; − 25.

Imagine that this note is picked up by a capable microphone and the resulting current properly amplified passes through an adjustable electrical filter and then to a distortionless loudspeaker. The filter is a network of coils and condensers which can be set to pass any desired range of frequencies and to eliminate all others. First, let the amplified current, corresponding to the fundamental, be the only component of the complex current to reach the loudspeaker. The fundamental alone is sounded by the loudspeaker. Next, set the filter to allow the passage also of the first overtone, which incidentally would be described as the "second harmonic" in most scientific papers. This component has a power two-tenths that of the fundamental. The two together then have a total power 1.2 times greater. Adding successively the other harmonics the total power becomes 1.236 times that of the fundamental alone. Since that ratio in decibels is 0.9, the intensity of the complex note is 0.9 db above the fundamental.

The question is: what effect do the harmonics have upon loudness? If the loudness level is determined for the fundamental pure note it will be found to be 36 db when its actual intensity is 40 db above reference intensity. This empirical result is conveniently obtained from the data on the loudness of pure tones which is plotted on page 241. For a fundamental of 392 cycles the loudness level is always less than the intensity level. When the overtones are added the intensity rises from 40 to 40.9 db. The loudness level which corresponds, as determined in Bell Laboratories, is 44 db. Whereas for the fundamental alone the 1000-cycle reference tone would be equally loud at 36 db, for the entire complex note the reference tone would have to be at the level of 44 db. The addition of the overtones raises the intensity from 40 to 40.9 but raises the loudness level from 36 to 44, a matter of 8 db. The overtones made the actual power 1.236 times greater but effectively, so far as loudness [1] is concerned, increased it 6 times.

The effects of the overtones for this violin string are typical for all musical notes with frequencies in the range below 700 cycles, where loudness levels differ most from intensity levels. For very low notes the loudness may be due almost entirely to the overtones. Fletcher gives the data for a piano note of 131 vibrations per second. The frequency ratios of its components are the same as for a violin string but their intensities, calling the fundamental unity and starting with it, are: 1; 0.46; 0.10; 0.12; 0.03; 0.31; 0.03; 0.10; 0.04; 0.04. The corresponding frequencies in cycles per second are: 131; 262; 393; 524; 655; 786; 917; 1048; 1179; 1310. Imagine that the note is played very softly, or heard from quite a distance, so that at the listener's ear the fundamental would have by itself an intensity only 30 db above the

---

[1] Because the contributions of its overtones to the loudness of a complex tone the elimination of the higher overtones—as in a home radio set—not only affects the quality of the note but also its loudness; and hence it alters to some extent the relation of loudness of successive notes in a musical composition.

reference intensity of 10^{-16} watt. The intensity levels
for all the components, expressed in decibels above the
reference are then as follows: 30; 26.6; 20; 20.8; 14.8;
24.9; 14.8; 20; 16; 16. It is interesting to consider what
would be the loudness level of each one of these components if it were sounded alone. These various loudness
levels are most conveniently read off from a chart similar to that on page 241. The levels are: -7; 8; 11; 16;
15; 25; 15; 20; 16; 16.

For the fundamental itself the loudness level is -7.
That is, a 1000-cycle reference tone 7 db below its reference level would be equally loud; but under that condition it would be below the threshold of audibility.
In other words, for this condition the fundamental of
the piano note can not be heard at all. Why one should
think he hears the pitch of the fundamental must await
the later discussion of page 113. The loudness of the
note is entirely due to its overtones; and those in the
middle range of frequencies contribute most.

When there are known the loudness levels which the
components would have when sounded individually the
loudness level for the note as a whole may be computed,
but by methods which are beyond the scope of the present discussion. The experimental results, however, are
available in this particular case where Fletcher reports
the loudness level to be 37 db above reference intensity. The total intensity of the piano note is increased
about 3.5 db by the inclusion of the harmonics, and a
note inaudible in its fundamental is given a loudness
level higher than its actual intensity. Of such importance in loudness are the harmonics of low musical
notes.

In the investigation of the loudness of complex tones synthetic notes were used as well as those natural to musical instruments. Separate generators of pure sinusoidal currents pooled their several currents, each separately controlled in intensity, to produce a complex sound. The methods will be discussed later. For the moment one experimental result is of interest: Ten pure tones, with frequencies in harmonic ratios, no one of which had an intensity sufficient to make it audible by itself, when combined produced an audible musical tone. Under some conditions, as to the frequency series of the individual pure tones, all the components could be equally below the thresholds, corresponding to their frequencies, by as much as 6 or 8 db and still in combination result in an audible musical tone with a definitely recognizable pitch, corresponding to the lowest frequency in the harmonic series.

The explanation of such phenomena is still in the hands of the research workers and apparently still incomplete. Indications are to be found in recent literature, however, that an adequate and comprehensive theory may soon appear. It will explain quantitatively what takes place in the inner ear.

Qualitatively, the ear is composed of three chambers, shown in the diagram on page 243. The outer ear includes the canal and terminates in the drum. The middle chamber contains the three tiny bones which by lever action transmit the pressures picked up by the drum to the liquid contents of the third chamber, the cochlea. In the process the pressure variations are multiplied thirty to sixty times, practically in the ratio in which a communication engineer would design a transformer mechanism to work between a very light medium like air and a dense one like water.

The lever structure of hammer, anvil and stirrup terminates in the flat footplate of the stirrup, through which pressure variations are imposed on the liquid of the cochlea. The cochlea itself, as its name implies, is a bony cavity shaped like a snail shell of two and three quarter turns and like that narrowing as it spirals. Starting at the lower and large end it is divided through almost all of its length by partitions which form three long narrow chambers. In cross-section the partitions follow the lines one would make by cutting a single piece of pie, starting with a cut which divides the whole into halves. The part of the first cut which is not necessary to free the piece represents a bony partition which carries the nerves. The continuation of this cut is the basilar membrane and the remaining radial line is another but nervously unimportant membrane. The wedge-shaped chamber has its own liquid contents but the membrane is so thin that for all dynamical consideration it may be disregarded. In effect, then, the cochlea is divided by a diametrical partition which separates its fluid contents for almost its entire length. Part of this partition is formed by the basilar membrane which contains the nerve ends that pick up the vibrations. (A diagram is shown on page 243.)

At the wide end these semi-circular chambers are closed by membranes across windows, or openings, in the bony structure. The upper, or oval, window is almost completely closed by the stirrup footplate and the membrane acts as a gasket to prevent leakage of the liquid into the middle ear as the stapes slides in and out. Incidentally the actual motion is very minute because the window is small and the lever system sacrifices distance of travel to gain in force. At the lower, or round, window the membrane serves to give elasticity to the wall of the cochlea and thus to take up any pressures which reach it through the liquid as the result of the piston-like motion of the stapes.

The whole mechanism is very small. Its length is about 31 millimeters. The connecting passageway at the distant end, the helicotrema, is only about a quarter of a square millimeter in area—not an opening through which rapid alternations in liquid pressure can be transmitted efficiently. The upper chamber, or scala vestibuli, and also the lower, or scala tympani—so called because the membrane across the round window is sometimes called a secondary ear drum—in their largest sections are less than two square millimeters and for most of the way less than one. At the windows they widen to three and to two square millimeters, respectively. The basilar membrane with its twenty-odd thousand rods (of Corti), each with twelve or more cilia, has a width between two and five tenths of a millimeter.

Sound waves received by the ear drum are transmitted through the oval window to the fluid of the upper section of the cochlea. If the pitch of the note is low, the fluid probably surges slowly back and forth through the narrow opening of the helicotrema while the membrane of the round window vibrates slowly in opposite phase to the stapes, bowing out while the stapes move in. At such a low pitch as 16 or 20 vibrations per second there would then be no vibration of the basilar membrane, no stimulus of its cilia, and no audition.

When higher frequencies of vibration are imposed upon the liquid of the upper section more of the energy passes through the thin basilar membrane which separates the sections. At what point along its length the greatest part of the energy takes the short cut, in preference to the long route to the helicotrema and back, depends upon the frequency and upon the vibrational characteristics of the basilar membrane. It appears that the higher the frequency the shorter the cut. Whereas vibrations of 100 cycles per second are largely transmitted by bending the membrane two or three millimeters from its extreme end, those of 1000 cycles pass at about the middle; and vibrations above 10,000 cycles flex the membrane immediately adjacent to the oval window. Where the vibration of the membrane is greatest there, of course, is the greatest stimulation of the nerve ends. These relationships are illustrated on page 243.

Corresponding to the frequency there is a spatial pattern to the vibration of the basilar membrane. This pattern becomes more complicated for complex sounds and also covers a greater area for greater intensity. A report as to the pattern is sent to the brain by those cilia which are affected and there, by affecting the areas where their nerves terminate, produces a space pattern which is part of the basis for the sensation of audition. The rate at which the nerves fire and the number which shoot constitute the remainder of the information on the basis of which the brain perceives. The nerves are said to fire at a definite point in the cycle of vibration but only in case the amplitude of vibration is sufficient to stimulate their discharge.

That the overtone structure of a complex sound is

represented in the inner ear by the space pattern of the vibration of the basilar membrane has been quite commonly accepted for many years. It is also believed that the brain perceives the pattern more or less as a whole and in proportion to the nerve discharges it receives; and so it draws the conclusion as to loudness which experiment has found. But most of the details of how it does so still remain to be discovered.

8 OVERLOADING AND DISTORTION

Overloading is the common ill to which vibrating systems are liable. It either occurs, or becomes manifest, during translation although its causes may be deep-seated. The diagnostic symptom is a lack of veracity which may escape the inexpert in mild cases but in severe cases is easily recognized. Treatment, after the cause has been located, usually involves a reduction of the power flow at that point to avoid overstrain. Thereafter the system will speak more truly but more faintly. If it should then be unable to reach its regular audience serious operations must be performed or a system of another design be employed.

When the system is that of the human ear it must be accepted as the common lot; its potentialities appreciated and allowances made for its limitations. A loudspeaker when overloaded radiates sounds which are not present in the current variations which are supplied to it. A vacuum-tube amplifier, which is supplied with a greater input than its characteristic warrants, acts to the overload as a modulator, not as a distortionless amplifier; and into its output introduces currents of frequencies which are not present in the input. The ear mechanism, under analogous conditions, reports to the brain the presence of vibrations which are not occurring at all in the air outside its drum. Its action gives rise to subjective tones—sounds real enough to the brain but having no counterpart of vibration outside the head and no external source of sound.

The point where this distortion—for such it is—takes place is apparently the middle ear. The lever system of ossicles, with names from the smithy, must move one way when the eardrum bows in and the opposite when it springs out. The two motions might well depart from exact symmetry when the amplitude of vibration is large. An inward motion of the drum from its position of rest might produce a different displacement of the footplate than would an equal motion outward. Compression need not be equal to extension for large displacements, even if it is for small. In the ear it appears to depart from equality when the sound intensity at the ear is higher than about 40 db above reference intensity.

This phenomenon is analogous to what happens electrically in a vacuum-tube amplifier. An amplifier has an output identical in frequency and proportional in amplitude to its input, as long as that input does not exceed certain operational limits determined largely by the tube's characteristics.

A vacuum tube, as its name implies, is one which has been freed as far as possible of molecules of gas or vapor. It is also an electronic device, depending for its action upon those tiny particles of negative electricity which are elements in the composition of all kinds of atoms. In metals there are always innumerable wandering electrons which stray from their atomic homes and engage in undirected and haphazard motions in the wide-open spaces between the atoms. In their motion they will generally dodge the more stable groups or swing through and past them, but frequently in such a manner as to cause them to shift slightly in position. If the electrons are excited to more violent motion the whole material is correspondingly wrought up; it gets hotter, for the heat which it contains is inherent in the motion of all its particles, electronic or atomic.

When a current of electricity flows through a wire there is superimposed upon the haphazard motions of the electrons an additional and directed motion. The electrons, while persisting in individual vagaries, will drift under the influence of an electrical generator or battery. This drifting constitutes a current; and the strength of the current depends upon the rate at which electrons are moving along, specifically, upon the net number per second that pass through any cross-section of the wire.

A current in a wire is a pellmell stream of electrons; and some of them may get going so fast as to break completely away from the wire and issue into surrounding space. There they will have an independent existence and move about like the molecules of a gas. Such a "thermionic emission" of electrons is negligible at ordinary temperatures but appreciable at those of red or white heat. In effect, electrons are boiled out of a wire. An emission of electrons takes place in an ordinary electric lamp when its filament is white hot. In the lamp they are a by-product of the white-hot heat; in a vacuum tube they are similarly produced but for the specific purpose of taking part in electric currents between the various electrodes of the tube.

In the ordinary vacuum tube there are three metal elements, called electrodes, for they have wires leading through the glass to which external circuits may be connected. One of the electrodes, the filament, is heated electrically to a temperature where it efficiently emits electrons into the surrounding vacuum. At some distance from it is a plate; and between filament and plate the third electrode, a wire grid—the contribution of DeForest. The circuit which brings in the current that is to be amplified is connected to the filament and the grid; and the circuit which is to take it away, to filament and plate. The connections are made through transformers, operating on the principle described on page 26. Connected into the plate circuit, also, is a battery which makes the plate positive with respect to the filament. Being positive the plate attracts to itself a steady stream of electrons, which then proceeds around the circuit and back to the filament. The stream is steady, and hence the current it represents is constant, except as the grid is effective. This wire mesh is in a strategic position close to the filament; and changes in its electrical condition exert a disproportionate influence on the current in the plate-filament circuit.

In the operation of a vacuum tube as an amplifier it is ordinarily arranged that the grid shall never become electrically positive as compared to the filament. This is accomplished by the simple expedient of connecting a small battery between grid and filament with the negative terminal to the grid. Under these conditions the negative grid repels electrons and so subtracts from the pulling power of the battery which, making the plate positive, is drawing electrons from filament to plate. If the grid is now made slightly less negative it subtracts less; and there is an increase in the stream of electrons in the filament-plate circuit. Conversely, if the grid is made more negative it opposes more strongly the action of the plate; and the stream is decreased.

The circuit carrying the current which is to be amplified is connected so that its effect is imposed upon the grid. Electrons from the input circuit then swing into and out of the grid. When this current is alternating, as it is if speech-bearing, it will make the grid alternately slightly more negative and slightly less so.

When a speech-bearing current forces a few extra electrons upon the grid their presence decreases the plate-filament current because the added electrons repel those which the filament emits. Then in the back-swing these extra electrons leave the grid; it returns to its previous electrical condition; and the output current in the plate-filament circuit does the same. The grid, however, loses not only its excess but, as the back-swing continues, a number of electrons which are nominally its own. These rush out into the input circuit until the grid has lost as many as it had previously gained. Because of the deficiency the grid then attracts electrons from the filament toward itself. But these pass through its meshes and thus bring about an increase in the stream from filament to plate. The process then reverses; and so the surplus and deficiency of the grid succeed periodically, proportional in amount to the input current and with the same frequency. And so the plate current follows the variations of the input current but in an amplified form because of the strategic position of the grid.

That is the condition for distortionless amplification.

At any instant the output current is a definite number of times greater than the input current, that is the output, O, is equal to some amplification factor, say a, times the input, I. A plot of corresponding pairs of values of I and O will appear as a straight line. Because of that there is said to be a linear relation between them. The plot depicting the output-input relationship is known as the "characteristic" of the tube and its associated equipment.

For inputs larger than some definite amount the plot ceases to be a straight line; it starts to curve. When the input is above that limiting value operation is no longer along the straight portion of the characteristic; and the relationship is non-linear. What then happens to an alternating-current input can be calculated from the curvature; it can also be determined experimentally; but it will merely be told here.

The tube amplifies but with more or less distortion. It operates for the most part as an amplifier but also as a modulator. It can be made to operate primarily as a modulator, and only incidentally as an amplifier, by a few adjustments including alterations in the battery voltages applied to its electrodes. It will act as a modulator when its operation is most completely upon the curved portion of its characteristic where the distortion is greatest. Under those conditions if the input is a single sinusoidal current, corresponding to a pure tone, the output will be a complex current. In it there will be components which are harmonics of the input, with frequencies 1, 2, 3, 4, and so on times that of the original sinusoid.

To a single-frequency current the tube will then act

as a harmonic generator. From its output, by using proper electrical filters, pure sinusoidal currents of the harmonic frequencies may be obtained. In that general way is constructed the frequency doubler mentioned on page 82.

If the tube, conditioned for modulation, is supplied with an input composed of two sinusoidal components of different frequencies, a and b, components will be found in its output which are harmonics of a and b. More than that, there will be components with frequencies which are sums and differences of the frequencies a and b, that is $a + b$ and $a - b$. These components are sidebands. This is the same operation as that through which, in radio, sidebands are produced in the modulation of a carrier, a, by an audio-frequency, b.

When a vacuum-tube amplifier is overloaded and so acts more like a modulator it has in its output all these components but unless the overloading is considerable the most powerful components are the currents of frequency a, b, and so on of the input; the harmonics $2a$, $2b$ and so on, as well as the sidebands $a + b$, $a - b$, and so on, are much less powerful. A convenient check on an amplifier, therefore, is to see how powerful, relatively, is the harmonic component in the output when a single-frequency current constitutes the entire input. In the case of the amplifiers on the Philadelphia-Washington circuit, which was described in the chapter on "Translation and Transmission", the harmonic component was 40 db, or more, below the fundamental, that is less than one ten-thousandth of its power. When those amplifiers handled an input of several frequencies, similarly negligible were the components in the output which had frequencies the sum and the difference of the input frequencies. The musical tones, in other words, did not modulate each other. There was no "cross-modulation" during transmission.

If transmission is to be distortionless, amplifiers en route must not act to any appreciable extent as modulators. There must be apparent no cross-modulation and no production of harmonics. When, however, the conditions are adjusted to favor modulation rather than distortionless amplification, or when the input seriously overloads, then a vacuum-tube amplifier produces not only these harmonics and cross-modulation products, with frequencies having values equal to the sum and the difference of the components it is to amplify, but also modulation products, sums and differences, involving the higher harmonics, such as $2a + b$, $2a - b$, $2b + a$, $2b - a$, and so on.

Starting with only two or three strong components in its input a badly overloaded amplifier, or loudspeaker, can make a veritable hash of music; and too frequently one or the other, or both at once, do just that. There oughta be a law——

When the ear does it, that's different; there really is a good deal in having the hash made at home; and also it takes rather careful argument sometimes to prove that it is a mess. Such argument will now be attempted.

Suppose the ear is listening to a single pure tone, how is one to prove that the brain at the same time perceives higher overtones? The proof requires a search tone and an application of the principle which underlies beats. If the second harmonic—that of double frequency as the engineers use the word—is reaching the brain, beats should be recognizable when there is simultaneously imposed upon the ear a pure tone almost the frequency of this second harmonic. The experiment, therefore, consists in supplying to the ear, preferably through head phones, a known intensity of a single-frequency current. Superimposed upon this is another sinusoidal current which is variable in frequency and intensity. This second current, the search current, is varied continuously in frequency from below to several octaves above that of the first current. If, when it approaches a frequency twice that of the first, there are recognizable beats, which become less and less rapid until the search frequency is exactly twice the original and then increase in rapidity until they are no longer perceptible, one can only conclude that within the inner ear a vibration of twice the frequency of the original pure tone is being imposed upon the basilar membrane. It probably got there because of the non-linear characteristics of the middle ear; but anyway, it is there in all cases where the intensity of the original tone is high enough.

Work in Bell Laboratories years ago showed that a note of 500 cycles per second will be accompanied in the brain by its double-frequency harmonic when the pure note has an intensity at the eardrum which is 41 db above its threshold level. The triple-frequency harmonic will appear when the 500-cycle note is 53 db above the threshold; the fourth harmonic at 68, and the fifth at 78. The more the ear is overloaded the greater its distortion and the more subjective becomes the brain's interpretation of the air vibrations outside. For frequencies below 500 cycles the harmonics appear at even lower levels above threshold; and for higher frequencies at slightly higher levels.

That distortion tones may exist in surprising number was shown by another series of careful experiments carried out some years ago. An eardrum was subjected simultaneously to two pure tones, one of 1200 cycles and the other of 700 but both at a level of 80 db. To determine what subjective tones were present a third tone could be added at the frequency to beat with one of the subjective tones if it existed. By varying the frequency of this search tone, the presence of the following tones was determined: the 700-cycle tone and its harmonics, namely 700, 1400, 2100 and 2800; the 1200-cycle tone similarly, 1200; 2400; 3600; and cross-modulations, namely, $700 + 1200 = 1900$; $1400 + 1200 = 2600$; $1200 - 700 = 500$; $2400 - 700 = 1700$; $1400 + 2400 = 3800$; $2400 - 1400 = 1000$; and others including 200, 900, 3100, 3300 and 4300.

Sixteen subjective tones, at least, resulted from two physical, or objective, tones. There were probably even more in the 0-4300 region which was investigated. Today with more refined experimental methods, extending higher in frequency, many more tones would probably be found. But sixteen is enough to point the moral: Electrical equipment permits the production of tones of relatively enormous intensities. It is today possible for conductors who employ such equipment to impose upon the ears of their audiences very intense tones and thus to produce subjective tones which are not experienced in the music ordinarily obtained from manually operated instruments. Such subjective tones are real to a listener; and if music is made louder there will be more of them. The composer and conductor of the future may have to allow for such effects.

Subjective tones are in the nature of self-deception, although no moral stigma is implied. The subject comes to believe that something is so which isn't. And as a result he may fail to recognize something which is. The failure is conveniently described in the literature as the result of "masking". If a single pure tone of any audible frequency is sounded it will mask more or less any other simultaneous tone of a different frequency.

The greatest effect of obscuring another tone will occur when the second tone is nearly the same frequency as the first or nearly that of one of its harmonics. Whether or not the first tone will completely mask a second depends upon their intensities. A tone of 800 cycles, if it has an intensity of about 85 db, will prevent the ear perceiving any tone in the entire frequency range from 600 to 4000 cycles per second for which the intensity is less than 30 db.

Low-pitched, but intense, tones can mask practically the range of higher frequencies. High-pitched tones, on the other hand, have little masking effect on tones of lowest pitch. It is easier to carry on a conversation against a high-pitched noise than a low one, against the shriller note of a locomotive whistle than the deep bay of an ocean liner.

When the second tone is very near to the frequency of the masking tone its existence may be indicated by beats. In the same way it may be perceived through beats when its pitch is very close to the octave or to some other harmonic of the first tone. A little higher, or lower, in frequency than will produce audible beats, and the second tone may be completely masked. As an example, if one listens to a pure tone of 1200 cycles at about 80 db above reference intensity and if at the same time another tone competes for auditory recognition, the second tone will have to be at a level of 62 or 64 db to be perceived if its frequency is either 1100 or 1300 cycles. But it need not be more than 54 db if its frequency differs from 1200 by only three or four cycles. Typical results for two different tones are plotted on page 245.

In the telephonic investigation of masking a very practical question was answered. When one listens with one ear pressed against a receiver, what is the effect of noise entering the free ear? Do the same masking and interference occur when two tones are introduced into opposite ears instead of both into the same ear? This required an investigation of binaural masking as contrasted to the monaural which has been described. Monaurally, a 1300-cycle tone needs to be 10,000 times (40 db) louder than is necessary for its unmasked audition in order to be perceived in the presence of a 1200-cycle tone about 60 db above reference. Binaurally, if one can just perceive a 1300-cycle tone in one ear he can continue to do so, despite the imposition upon the other ear of a 1200-cycle tone, until the 1200-cycle tone is raised to a power a million times greater than is necessary for its bare perception. When one is telephoning what one hears with the free ear probably does not mask at all unless it is so very intense that by bone conduction it gets transmitted to the telephoning ear.

What goes through the head gets to the other ear about 50 db lower in power level. For example, if a telephone receiver is applied to the deaf ear of a person who has unilateral deafness he will begin to recognize the presence of a tone in the receiver when its intensity is about 50 db higher than would be required if it supplied his good ear.

One of the most interesting and important instances of subjective tones occurs in cases where the brain is convinced as to the presence of the fundamental of a note when the fundamental is not present in the vibrations imposed upon the eardrum. This is an opposite sort of an effect to the hearing of harmonics which are not existent. Unlike the subjective tones so far described, it requires no high intensity to produce it.

The effect, as was implied on page 9, might have been discovered at any time during the last hundred years but it was first noticed during the telephonic investigation of hearing. Let the note of a musical instrument be picked up by a microphone and supplied through an adjustable filter to a receiver or loudspeaker. Set the filter to cut out components of the total current which have the frequencies of the fundamental and of its first three or four harmonics. Listen to the sound. It will not be quite that of the musical instrument because of this distortion. Then ask what is the pitch of the note that issues from the loudspeaker. Check the answer by striking on a piano the note nearest in pitch. The piano note will not be the note corresponding to the lowest frequency harmonic that passes the filter; instead it will be the note corresponding to the missing fundamental.

In the air adjacent to the ear, in the middle ear, and in the vibration pattern of the basilar membrane there is no vibration corresponding in frequency to the fundamental; and yet the brain asseverates that stimulus. Run the loudspeaker as low as desired or as loud, it makes no difference; the brain has supplied the fundamental from the pattern due to the higher overtones. It would appear that the brain is capable of supplying substitutes for the harmonic terms which the filter has suppressed; the substitutes have the proper frequencies but not the proper intensities to recreate the series. The sensation of pitch, therefore, accords with the original note but the quality, or timbre, is not the same.

After this effect was discovered a series of vacuum-tube oscillators was set up in Bell Laboratories which permitted the synthesis of any desired combination of ten sinusoidal currents of frequencies 100, 200 and so on to 1000 cycles. When equal currents were simultaneously supplied to a telephone receiver the listener heard a full 100-cycle tone. Eliminating the 100-cycle fundamental produced no noticeable effect. In fact if any five consecutive frequencies were present the pitch was always judged to be 100 cycles. When the components had frequencies of 200, 400, 600, 800 and 1000 the pitch was, of course, 200 cycles; and this still seemed to be the pitch when only the 600-, 800-, and 1000-cycle currents were combined. Combinations like 100, 300, 500, 700 and 900 had no definite pitch and had the quality of noise; similarly for combinations like 100, 400, 700 and 1000 or like 200, 500, 800 and 1000.

The ability of the brain to deceive itself as to the existence of the fundamental and the lower harmonics of a musical note, when five or more consecutive upper harmonics are present, explains certain past situations in the phonograph arts. Until 1925 phonographs and talking machines recorded and reproduced only the narrow band of frequencies from 350 to 3000 cycles, a range slightly more than three octaves. Very few of the upper harmonics of musical notes and of human speech were included; and none of their lowest notes.

The records were cut by the energy of the sound waves themselves, with the result that notes or harmonics which were too weak to drive the graver were lost in the process. The graver was operated by a diaphragm at the small end of a horn which served to collect the sound. Around its open end, when orchestral music was being recorded, there had to be tightly grouped in an unnatural arrangement all the instrumentalists. The most sound practicable was required; and even the instruments were altered for the occasion. The violins had to be Strohs in which the bridge vibrates a diaphragm at the end of a small horn—and this horn was directed into that of the recording machine. Naturalness and fidelity were sacrificed; and the result was "canned music".

Improvement came from the adoption of "electrically-cut" records which were by-products, in equipment and techniques, of various telephonic researches. A condenser microphone picked up the sound without requiring unnatural rearrangements of its sources; a vacuum tube amplified the resulting current; and an electro-mechanical device, involving the principles of the motor element of a loudspeaker, drove the graver. All the power that was needed was available. The first records cut by this method tolerated a much wider range of sound intensity, preserved fainter notes, and covered a frequency range of about five octaves. In more recent years the range has been extended to somewhat higher frequencies; and there have been other improvements which will be discussed in the chapter on "Recording Sound".

During the first quarter of the century the quality of the speech and music from phonographs was unmistakably unnatural. An unconscious and unrecognized savior of the industry was the human ear, or more strictly the brain to which it led. Listeners to phonographs *heard* low notes and recognized their pitches even though their fundamental and lower overtones were not on the records and were not in the emitted sound. Subjective tones covered some of the shortcomings of the equipment. With present-day apparatus subjective impressions of non-existent pitches are no longer necessary. Low notes can be recorded and reproduced with surprising fidelity to the actual frequencies and to the intensities of their lower harmonics.

The electro-acoustical apparatus of today, however, is making more important another phenomenon of hearing which is somewhat in the nature of a subjective effect. Like that just described it concerns the interpretation of pitch. Under most conditions it is safe to say, and has been so assumed for centuries, that pitch is merely the name for the sensation which corresponds to vibration frequency. Pitch, accordingly, has an exact equivalent in vibration frequency; and whenever two notes have the same pitch they have the same frequency within the limits of the minimum perceptible increment. Pitch has been generally supposed, also, to be independent of overtone structure.

The experiments reported in the last few pages, however, have shown that pitch is influenced by overtone structure, and dependent upon it in many instances. That it is also not independent of intensity has been noticed by occasional observers but the fact never attracted much attention. It has not as yet been fully investigated; and, indeed, there was little reason for doing so and no suitable apparatus until there were built such high-power loudspeakers as those described on page 74. Those instruments can radiate into the air vibrations of tremendous acoustical power, which are faithful translations into sound waves of their electrical currents.

Using that equipment it has been found that the sensation of pitch for a pure tone depends upon its intensity. For power levels of more than 50 db above reference intensity the ear fails to ascribe to a vibration a sensation of pitch which is equal to its frequency. For frequencies below 2000 cycles it rates pitch lower than frequency; and for higher frequencies makes a slight mistake in the opposite direction. For greater intensities the deviation is larger.

Although the data are as yet incomplete the maximum variation appears to be in the frequency region between 100 and 200 cycles. Above this region the variation between mind and matter is progressively less to about 2000 cycles. The test is, of course, to be made by referring the sensation caused by the high-power tone to a reference sensation of a low-power tone, the pitch of which can be adjusted. Starting with a 150-cycle tone at a level of 68 db, S. S. Stevens at Harvard found that its pitch is the same as a low-power tone of 147 cycles, a difference of two percent. If the power level of the 150-cycle tone as it reaches the ear is 76 db the frequency of the reference tone has to be reduced to 145 cycles to be equal in pitch. At 93 db to 134, a difference between physical fact and mental appraisal of eleven percent.

In one of his published papers Fletcher describes the pitch relationship of two pairs of tones. A pure tone of 200 cycles at 40 db gave the same sensation of pitch as one of 222 cycles at 100 db. A pure tone of 400 cycles at 40 db had the same pitch as one of 421 cycles at 100 db. This means that a very intense vibration at 222 cycles produces the same sensation of pitch as a moderate vibration of 200 cycles; and similarly for the intense at 421 cycles and the moderate at 400. The 400-cycle tone is, of course, the octave of the 200-cycle. Is the 421 cycle tone an octave above the 222-cycle? Fletcher found that when sounded successively they were judged to be an octave apart. Past experience dealing with tones of moderate intensities has taught that tones separated by an octave should be consonant; but these intense tones when sounded together proved to be very dissonant.

The intensity level of 50 db, where this departure of pitch from a one-to-one correspondence with frequency begins to be noticeable, corresponds to about one hundred-thousandth of the maximum power which a full orchestra may deliver to the ear. The maximum power is about one hundred decibels above reference intensity; and at that level the ear is exposed to very severe changes in pressure despite the fact that the intensity is about 30 db below the threshold of feeling. When orchestral music is amplified and reproduced by powerful loudspeakers, the level may be even higher than 100 db; it gets uncomfortably close sometimes to the threshold of feeling.

It is safe to say, therefore, that this phenomenon of a shifting of pitch with increasing intensity is one which will demand attention of directors and composers and may be of some importance in the music of the future.

PART THREE

AN ELECTRICAL FUTURE FOR MUSIC

10   THE POWER OF MUSIC

Music hath power but surprisingly little except when it is played on the big bass drum. When facilities are to be provided for the transmission of its sounds, or for their recording and reproduction, the communication engineer needs to know the amount of power for which he must make provision. He is particularly concerned with the peaks of power for at those moments the electro-acoustical system, unless adequately designed, is in danger of overloading with consequent distortion of the music it is transmitting. The information he is collecting will ultimately have value also for composer and director.

The problem of determining the power of musical instruments, and of their assemblies, has been attacked in a statistical manner. Tests have been conducted to determine the average power and the peaks which occur under typical conditions. To what heights above the average do the peaks rise and what is the percentage of them at various levels? The results read like a description of a mountain range which has a certain average altitude above sea, or reference, level and has such and such percentage of its peaks between various specified levels. But the parallel ends there, because the engineer wishes to know also how the extremes of power are ordinarily distributed through the entire range of audible frequencies.

Some of the scientists in Bell Laboratories recently developed a method which permits them to make about 240 separate measurements a minute of the maximum power in a sound. Just as mountainous peaks might be classified in groups 8-9 thousand, 9-10 thousand, and so on feet above sea level, so the engineer adopts levels convenient to him and therefore expressed in decibels. What he detects is the acoustic pressure of the sound and he sets his levels so that there is a new level class every time the pressure doubles which corresponds to a quadrupling of power.

A microphone picks up the music of some instrumental solo, converting it into current which passes through a system of vacuum-tube amplifiers. It emerges at a higher electrical pressure, that is "voltage" to use the usual technical term. The voltage is applied simultaneously to ten parallel circuits, each containing a "relay tube".[1] Associated with each tube is a mechani-

[1] In these tubes there takes place a phenomenon much like a lightning discharge through air. In the air there are always wandering around some electrons which have been set free by ultraviolet light, cosmic rays or other ionizing forces. When a voltage builds up between a cloud and the earth they are given a directed motion. The higher the voltage the more they are accelerated. If it is high enough they attain speeds that make their collisions with the air molecules destructive. They can knock off an outermost electron. And this freed electron, starting off under the influence of the voltage, also attains a destructive speed. And so almost in an instant a nonconductive air path has become conducting and it continues conducting even though the voltage drops immediately to a value way below that necessary to initiate the lightning flash. Relay tubes, therefore, have properly designed amounts of easily ionizable gas. A steady voltage is applied to them which is just insufficient to start a discharge. Superimposed upon this is the voltage under measurement. If it happens to have an instantaneous peak—no matter for how short a time—it starts the discharge; and current flows to operate the counter.

cal counter like the odometer of an automobile. If the voltage is high enough to operate the relay tube the counter turns an added digit. The tubes are adjusted to act like triggers to the applied voltage but they are successively adjusted to require higher voltages. Starting with the tube that trips at the least voltage, the next requires double the voltage, and so on to the last which will operate only for voltages 512 times larger. By noting what counters have been affected two levels are indicated between which lies the voltage under measurement.

As the tests are usually conducted a professional musician plays on his instrument some piece of music selected to indicate its ordinary range of notes and loudness. The "peak-amplitude" meter meanwhile records the peaks of voltage which correspond to the peaks of pressure in the sound. The device records the highest voltage during an eighth of a second. Records are made of the peaks in alternate eighths of a second during the several minutes required for playing the musical selection. In a matter of only four minutes, 960 measurements will record themselves. That is enough, particularly when the results on several other selections are taken into account, to give very good statistical data. No measurements are made during the intervening eighths because that time is required for the automatic resetting of the triggers.

While these peak measurements are being made a grosser measurement is also going on. This gives the average power as integrated over periods of fifteen seconds. During a period of this length there may be pauses in the music as well as the usual variations in intensity from note to note. The measurement, however, tells what steady pressure the sound would have had to exert for the transfer during the fifteen seconds of the same total amount of energy. The average power for each instrumental solo is used as the reference intensity to which are referred the intensities of the various peaks.

One of the reasons for finding the average power during the determinations of the peaks is to insure that succeeding tests in the series are carried out under essentially identical conditions. After completion of the test already described, an electrical filter is introduced into the circuit so that only currents of a definite narrow band of frequencies are passed from the microphone to the peak-amplitude meter. The musician then repeats the selection and the counters show the various peaks in that frequency band. The average power during the encore should be about that of the first rendering—within one or two db, which is about the average variation for some musicians in fifteen repetitions. The filters are changed for each playing until the range of audible frequencies is covered.

By this method tests were made for the more important musical instruments and the big bass drum came out ahead. Its peak power was found to be 25 watts and it radiated that much power in six percent of the one-eighth second intervals during which its performance was studied. The piano has a peak power only one hundredth of the drum, 0.25 watt; but it will reach that peak in sixteen percent of the measurements. Flute, piccolo and clarinet have even less powerful peaks, about one-fifth those of the piano. Cymbals will originate their peak power, of 9 or 10 watts, seven or more percent of the time.

These results were obtained from a very few musical selections but those chosen were representative of the instruments, included extremes of range and volume and included also various techniques of playing. The total powers were obtained by calculation from the measured voltages; and they involve some assumptions as to the distribution of sound in the space immediately around a musician and his instrument. They are not to be considered exact in the sense in which the computation of an income tax must be, but rather to be within the reasonable error of a refined experiment of this type.

The study of the levels at which peaks occurred in each frequency band developed a mass of data, a few examples of which will be quoted. Cymbals reach their highest peaks at frequencies above 8000 cycles. The triangle, which in peak power is comparable to a clarinet, has its maximum in the interval between 5600 and 8000 cycles, while for the clarinet two or three percent of the peaks are in the octave above middle C. The trombone has its highest peaks in the interval 2000-2800 cycles and in that between 500 and 700. Its peak power is relatively large, being about a quarter of that for a 36 by 15 inch bass drum.

The piano is an exception among musical instruments because the peak of its power in the range of frequencies represented by the octave above middle C is practically equal to its peak power. For most instruments the peak power is several times greater than the peak in any narrow range of frequencies, as is to be expected, since the peak is the total of the contributions, at the instant, for all the frequency ranges. For the piano about one sixth of the peaks occur in the octave above middle C; and their average value is practically the same as the average of all the peaks the instrument attains.

Peak-power investigations have also been made of the human voice; in fact, because the researches were for telephonic application, they preceded the study of musical instruments. For speech the average power is about ten microwatts. Of the one-eighth second intervals two percent will be 20 db (100 times) higher, indicating peak power in the voice as high as 1000 microwatts. Peaks of ten times the average power are most frequent, occurring more than ten percent of the time. More than twenty percent of the time the peak power of speech is below the average power, as is to be expected due to pauses and to the consonants which have only a tenth to a thousandth of the power of the vowels. For speech, on the average, most of the power is found to be in the components which lie between 250 and 1000 cycles for male voices, and between 500 and 1500 for female. Less than a quarter of one percent of the power in women's speech is below 125 cycles; and only about four percent in masculine speech. Above 2000 cycles the percentages are five and seven for men and women, respectively. Frequencies as high as 8000 are important in speech but the power of the corresponding components is very little. In the region of high frequencies are the sounds like *th*at, *th*in, *v*at, *f*or, *s*it and *z*ip which are so easily missed even under the best of acoustic conditions.

The vowels contribute the loudness to speech; but its intelligibility depends upon the initial and final consonants of the syllables. The vowel sounds show two pronounced and characteristic regions of frequency apiece, as illustrated by the chart on page 246. It is the vowels that are most important in the singing voice; the consonants are usually disregarded or left to the imagination of the auditors. In singing, because the art is concerned with the production of musical tones and their esthetic and emotional consequences, the throat can, and must, be used in a way which is impracticable in speech, where articulation and maximum intelligibility are of greatest importance. The result is less tightness and tension in the throat, fuller tone and greater volume. Whereas one hundred microwatts is about the average power in a spoken vowel during ordinary speech, ten thousand times as much, that is a whole watt, appears from recent tests to be the power in a sung vowel. That means two to four times the average power of a piano.

The power of the singing voice is reported[1] to be greater at the higher pitches. For both men and women the full-voice power can rise to one watt for their higher notes. A curve on page 248 shows the relationship. From the data so far reported it would appear that women and men can radiate equal powers at pitches about an octave apart. They can put out 100 microwatts apiece at C_2 and C_1 respectively; and about a thousand times as much at G_1 and G. Just why has not as yet had

---

[1] In a paper by Wolf, Stanley, and Settee, in the "Journal of the Acoustical Society of America," April 1935. This journal is the best technical reference for the latest acoustical studies.

physical and physiological explanation. Such relatively large power outputs, however, are in accord with the recognized fact that solo voices can be heard over a large orchestra or chorus.

For orchestras several studies have been made by the telephone engineers. A heavy orchestra may deliver a peak power as high as 70 watts, about as much as three bass drums or a thousand flutes and piccolos. In several selections the peaks of a 75-piece orchestra were only 14 watts. An 18-piece orchestra may hit an occasional peak of 10-12 watts and a large number of 2-3 watts.

The average power of even a large orchestra is likely to be only about one-tenth of a watt. Average power, however, has very little significance except as a base line from which to measure the peaks. It is an easily measured physical magnitude but has no equivalent in sensation. In twenty sets of measurements on instrumental solos and six on orchestras the peaks were found to be between 17 and 34 db higher, generally between 20 and 28 db with an average of 24. It appears therefore that, on the average, peak power is about 250 times the average power. Such peaks occur probably only two or three percent of the time, dependent, of course, upon the musical selection. For ninety percent of the time the peaks to which music attains are less than 100 times the average power.

All these data as to peak power are basic to the proper design of electro-acoustical equipment and transmission facilities. The engineers, however, contrived another series of tests which served in part as checks on the data reported above but in main part as a source of further exact information as to what must be transmitted if music is to be adequately reproduced.

Instrumental solos were picked up in one sound-proof laboratory and reproduced in another by a loud-speaker of excellent and carefully determined character-istics. Actually, between 20 and 15,000 cycles the complete electro-acoustical system had a reproduction characteristic flat to about 2.5 db. In the circuit were filters of so-called "high-pass" and "low-pass" types. By the low-pass filter all components in the current which were above a predetermined frequency could be sup-pressed, so that they would not be present in the repro-duced sound. Similarly, by using the high-pass filter only components above some definite frequency would issue from the loudspeaker. The filter limits were ad-justable in each case.

Observers listened to the loudspeaker. Near it were two signal lamps, designated A and B. One or the other of these was lighted whenever music was issuing from the loudspeaker. In one case the observers listened to unfiltered transmission and in the other to reproduc-tion which by filtering had lost all components above some definite frequency or below some other frequency. Whether the unfiltered music corresponded to A or to B was known only to the engineers behind the scenes and it was changed from one to the other on a random basis. The observers knew merely that either reproduc-tion A or reproduction B was not complete. They listened alternately several times in succession to A and B and then recorded individually their judgment as to which was filtered. A new setting of the filter was then made, changing the cut-off, and the test was repeated.

This series of tests was very severe in its group judgments because most of the observers were in their early twenties and all had fully normal hearing. The music was reproduced at its natural loudness except for the more powerful instruments and each observer heard, except when the filter was in circuit, what he would have heard if he had been placed only a few feet from the musicians.

Tests were started with a filter adjustment which made an unmistakable difference between conditions A and B, such that at least ninety percent of the observers could correctly determine which was the filtered condition. Each test was repeated several times with random correspondence between the actual conditions and the A-B designations. Successive filter adjustments were made until statistically the judgments were fifty-fifty. That meant an average inability to detect the filter and an aural inability to appreciate the presence of the components which it suppressed. Sometimes as a check the lights were flashed as if the filtering condition had been changed when really both A and B were unfiltered transmissions. Whenever that happened the judgments were fifty-fifty, plus or minus four percent.

The engineers summarized their results on the basis that sounds, the filtering elimination of which could not be detected correctly in 60 percent of the judgments, were unimportant. For example, when high-pass filters eliminated from piano music all tones below 70 cycles the observers, as a class under examination, could only just make a passing grade of 60 percent on a true-false test basis. To raise their marks to 80 percent the question had to be made easier by cutting out all frequencies below 100 cycles. The group could make a passing grade of 60 percent when the low-pass filter let through only tones below 6500 cycles; and 80 percent when it passed only tones below 5500 cycles.

In listening to music in an auditorium, or to the music of several instruments simultaneously, it is probable that a person of normal hearing cannot tell whether or not the music is lacking frequencies above or below respectively the frequencies corresponding to these 80 percent correct judgments. What that means as to the music of various instruments appears from the chart on page 250. For the piano it means that the fundmentals of notes below G_2 are not heard, nor the first overtone of a note below G_3.

The musical sounds of instruments are, of course, accompanied by non-musical sounds such as the buzz of reeds, the hissing of air, key clicks, or lip noises. The experiments with filters gave an indication of the frequency region where such sounds are most noticeable. In a flute, for example on its highest register, the tones above 9000 cycles are accompanied by considerable noise of blowing. Because, in part, of that characteristic the observers could detect a difference between direct and electrically reproduced flute music unless tones up to about 13,000 cycles were transmitted. Substitute "bowing" for "blowing" and the last two sentences read equally well on the violin. In the oboe the noise blends so with the tone that there is no such definite region of noise in its note.

Most remarkable for the inclusion of a wide range of frequencies are such sounds as footsteps and hand clapping. Their range extends from about 80 to 15,000 cycles. The jingle of keys needs frequencies as high as

15,000 and in that respect is like the clash of cymbals, but cymbals extend an octave lower as would be expected from their relative size.

The net result of the various researches which this chapter has reported is to indicate definitely the frequency band which must be transmitted if there is to be reproduced for the ear all that it can hear [1] of an original sound. In general, for the notes of music, for speech, and for usual noises, there must be picked up, transmitted and translated into sound waves all components whose frequencies lie between 40 or 60 cycles and 14 or 15 thousand cycles.

In addition the ideal electro-acoustical system should handle extremes of power in the order of at least 70 db. That is the difference in level between the weakest and the most powerful sounds in the music of a full and heavy orchestra. An ideal system, therefore, should handle successively powers that are in this ratio of 10,000,000 to 1 without losing the faintest sound or distorting the strongest. This requirement was the minimum in the apparatus which permitted the reproduction described on page 74. That equipment recreated in the hall in Washington all the music, in all its extremes of power, which the ear could have heard in the Academy of Music in Philadelphia.

[1] Many listeners, of course, are satisfied with less complete reproduction. For further discussion see page 222.

"My God, it talks" was what the Emperor of Brazil said in 1876 when he heard the telephone in the exhibit of Alexander Graham Bell at the Centennial Exposition. An imperial judgment, spontaneously expressed, it attracted attention to a demonstration which the judges would have passed by. From that moment it got the crowd and recognition both popular and scientific.

There is no corresponding record of the bon mots of the magnates of the motion-picture industry when the movie started to talk. There is evidence that some may have missed the essential of that achievement.

To many who attended the early demonstrations in the auditorium of Bell Laboratories the marvel, if to their minds there was any, consisted in the synchronization of sound and scene. Synchronization was exact; sound issued from the loudspeakers in time with the action projected upon the curtain. Of course, synchronism never can be absolutely exact except for a definite distance from the curtain, because of the difference in speed of light and sound. It can be adjusted for any position in an auditorium but nearer than that to the stage the sound will be slightly ahead of the action and farther away, it will be behind, perhaps perceptibly.

The first sound pictures had their speech and music recorded on discs, by the method of electrically cutting which was mentioned on page 114. A microphone placed

133

in front of the actors picks up the speech which is then carried in the form of current variations through amplifiers to the recording device. This is an electrically operated graver which cuts a wavy line in a wax plate. The plate is mounted on a turntable and rotates at uniform speed against the graver. From this wax, by several intermediate processes, there are obtained the final records.

In reproduction a special transmitter is used, the diaphragm of which is driven by a phonograph needle. While this needle follows the delicate wave, which spirals as a fine line on the face of the record, it repeats the vibratory motion of the graver. The current in the transmitter, therefore, undergoes variations similar to those supplied to the graver. And this current after amplification produces from the loudspeaker sounds with the same characteristics of frequency and relative intensity as those that fell upon the original microphone.

Synchronization requires that the motion-picture camera and the turntable shall be driven at equivalent speeds and that corresponding marks be made on film and record to indicate the beginning of a scene. In reproduction the projector and the turntable carrying the record must run at equivalent speeds and the reproducer needle must start at its mark on the record at the moment the film reaches the proper position in the projector. Although these requirements necessitated considerable ingenuity of design the problems they presented were relatively unimportant.

The idea that a record of sound should accompany synchronously a record of scene was most obvious; and talking movies had been attempted years before. These earlier efforts had been attended by no success not because of difficulties of synchronization but because the reproduced sound was so incomplete in harmonics, so limited in range of intensity and so unmistakably a canned product that no illusion was possible. During the succeeding years the photographic art made rapid progress until its product was capable of creating in the minds of a motion-picture audience many of the emotions which would have been excited by the actual scene. An audience would only have been annoyed by sound accompaniments which were as deficient in naturalness as the phonograph records of the first quarter of this century.

What was necessary was a faithfulness in the recreated sound which would enhance the illusion of the pictures. Mechanisms became available in the condenser transmitter, described on page 60, the distortionless vacuum-tube amplifier, and certain adaptations of telephone receiver and transmitter to fit graver and pick-up needle. These developments were the fruit of years of research but the design of a suitable system for synchronization took only a relatively short time of a smaller group of workers. Through their designs camera and recording turntable can be driven by motors electrically interlocked, and the record turntable be geared to the projector. With that arranged, the talkies had their Broadway first night and the revolution was on.

The operation of recording sound is always one of converting a time-pattern into a space-pattern. It is the time relationship of the pressure upon one's eardrum which determines what he hears. For each succeeding instant there is a corresponding value of the air pressure. Successive values may be plotted against time, as a statistician plots cost of living or stock market prices. A horizontal length of line then indicates time; and a space-pattern on a piece of paper replaces a time-pattern. When the sound, itself, plots its own pressure while the paper moves uniformly at right angles the result is an oscillogram.

Such a pressure-time plot may be recorded on a smoked glass, as in Bell's early experiment, or on a flat disc, as in those of Edison, Berliner and others who first made phonograph records. The oscillogram of a phonograph disc may be recorded laterally or vertically. In the former case a keen eye can detect that the spiral line is wavy, swinging slightly back and forth in the plane of the record. In the latter case the line does not appear sinuous but its depth varies because the graver dug into the wax in proportion to the air pressure of the sound wave it recorded. Vertical cutting was the method of the Edison phonograph; and it is the method employed in the most recent improvement from Bell Laboratories. An oscillogram may also be traced as a wavy line on a photographic film; and this method is one of the two which are used when scene and sound are to be recorded on the same strip of motion-picture film.

The oscillographic methods of recording sound are the most obvious. Historically they were also the earliest. The next was the method of the telegraphone of Poulsen. In it an attempt was made to form in a steel wire a space-pattern of magnetism which should serve as a record of a time-pattern of sound pressure in air. The device had some commercial use but the speech reproduced from it was seriously distorted and far from natural.

The fundamental idea, however, that is involved in a magnetic pattern for sound, had interesting possibilities which, from time to time, attracted some attention in telephonic researches. Most telephonic equipment, in matter of fact, is electromagnetic; and the research program of that industry has always concentrated on the study of magnetism, the discovery of new magnetic alloys and the invention of new structures. Out of that work has come in very recent years an improved method of magnetic recording which permits the reproduction of speech and music with good quality, that is, about the same as that of present day radio broadcasting. Some details of this device will be given in the chapter on "Teaching Aids".

A third type of space pattern into which sound may be converted is chemical. A photographic record may be obtained in which the photographic density of the negative corresponds to the acoustic pressure. This method is generally described as that of "variable density", distinguishing it from the oscillographic method of recording on film which is "variable area".

A variable density "sound track" has certain similarities, in superficial appearance and in physical fact, to a sound wave. Imagine the sound wave of a single pure tone. Imagine further that at some instant every particle of air along its path is suddenly stopped in its then position. The frozen ripples which are to be found on the surfaces of small ponds after sharp cold spells are analogous, except that they represent waves up and down while in sound the particles move back and forth along the direction of propagation. Still in imagination one cuts from the frozen sound wave a long thin strip, a ribbon paralleling the direction of propagation; and dies or stains its air molecules for visibility. Examining this strip one finds at regular intervals—a wave length apart, in fact—congestions of the molecules and midway between these points a proportionate emptiness.

Next one sets a narrow slit across the molecular ribbon so that he can see only a small portion at a time; as if he looked out at a parade from a long narrow hallway. If he now draws the ribbon rapidly along behind the slit he can observe what takes place at a point in the path of such a sound. When the most molecules are visible through the slit the sound pressure at that point is greatest—a condensation has arrived; when the least, minimum pressure, corresponding to a rarefaction. If the ribbon passes the slit with the speed of sound in air, about 345 meters a second, the observer will see how the pressure varies with time. Instead of hearing, he will see the time-pattern of a sound.

To record the pattern a light may be placed behind the molecular ribbon to shine through the slit except as it is blocked by the molecules. Then in front of the slit a photographic film is drawn along at uniform speed, being exposed at each instant to an amount of light which depends upon the molecular congestion, that is, upon the acoustic pressure. It doesn't make any difference at what speed the film moves, provided it is steady; if very slowly as compared to the velocity of sound, the record will look like the sound track of a motion picture film as shown in Figure 25 on page 253.

The patterns for all pure tones will be alike except in two important details. The distance between similar states of affairs, which is proportional to the wave length, will be inversely as the frequency; half as much, for example, for the octave of a tone. The congestion of molecules will be greater, and the emptiness correspondingly greater, the more intense the sound which is recorded.

If a number of different pure tones with individual intensities are being transmitted simultaneously the pattern will be very complex. The vibratory motions of the molecules which transfer the acoustic energy are in such case the resultants, or combinations, of the several vibrations which would occur if each component traveled alone. Molecules of air, and electrons in wires, obey the law of superposition which generalizes this fact. Upon those two media innumerable sinusoidal vibrations may be imposed without mutual interference. It therefore becomes possible to add the effects, which several pure-tone components would produce, to find the total effect corresponding to a complex tone.

In consequence, the preceding picture of a sound pattern may be extended to cover complex sounds. Imagine molecular ribbons for each component. Place them side by side so that the light passes through them all to reach the slit. Then the picture which is formed upon the photographic film is a true record of the complex sound. In the variations of photographic density is preserved the pressure pattern of the sound.

In practice, since sound waves are difficult to freeze,

the time-pattern of the wave is converted as faithfully as possible into a time-pattern of electrons in a circuit; and that in turn into a space-pattern of one or another of the three main types, oscillographic, magnetic, or chemical. A microphone picks up the sound; its diaphragm, light in weight, responding to delicate variations in air pressure. The current properly amplified supplies the recording device.

In the oscillographic group, sometimes, the recording device is in substance a galvanometer element carrying a small mirror. A narrow beam of light is reflected from the mirror to fall as a spot on a screen or photographic film. When an alternating current causes the mirror to vibrate the spot performs a similar but larger vibration. If the film is moved uniformly the beam traces an oscillograph on the film.

In the chemical group there are two main possibilities. In one case the current from the microphone controls the intensity of a light which shines through a narrow slit to expose a fine line at right angles to the motion of the film. This is the method of the flashing lamp or Aeo light.

The more usual method, that in the Western Electric system for sound recording, makes use of a light valve. This is a slit formed by two thin ribbons of metal placed in a magnetic field. The sound-bearing currents pass through these ribbons; and the latter, following the law for current-carrying wires in a magnetic field, move to increase or decrease the slit formed by their separation. The width of the slit then varies in accordance with the current, proportionally to its strength. Upon the slit falls a steady beam of light; with the result that the amount which gets through is accurately determined by the current. The light that emerges is directed by a proper lens system to fall as a fine line across the film. As the film moves, therefore, successive narrow portions of it are exposed photographically in proportion to the current, and hence in proportion to the acoustic pressure actuating the microphone.

All these methods of recording sound for talking motion pictures rely for their practicability upon the vacuum-tube amplifier. Without amplification by that device the feeble current from the microphone would be unable to produce in the recording devices effects of sufficient magnitude. Without amplification the reproduced current could not operate high-power loudspeakers. Given the possibility of distortionless magnification of a sound-bearing current, and also the general advanced state of the communication arts to which the vacuum tube itself has been no mean contributor, and there became possible some of the things for which inventors have struggled prematurely.

Years after the light-valve method of recording was commercially adopted one of the patent attorneys of Bell Telephone Laboratories ran across a letter to the editor of the *Nation* complaining that an old man, Eugene Lauste, who had pioneered in the art of talking motion pictures was destitute while the industry prospered. He traced the letter, and verified its correctness.

Eugene Lauste then became a member of the technical staff of Bell Telephone Laboratories with two tasks, one to assemble such of his own apparatus as could be located, and by replacements to reconstruct the entire system which he had built in the early

1900's, and the other to assist the patent department by his knowledge of the prior art. On the day these lines happen to be written a complete reproduction of his system for sound pictures was presented to the Smithsonian Institution and accepted. It contains the first light valve and also various electro-mechanical devices with which he attempted to get the amplification without which his system, although operative, was commercially impractical. He was an inventor ahead of his time; but in his latter years his work became known and he was honored by his younger colleagues, as for example with an honorary membership in the Society of Motion Picture Engineers.

Reproduction from the sound track which he obtained by his method had to be accomplished by using a selenium cell. This is a device which is light sensitive and gives rise to an electric current when illuminated. From present-day viewpoints it is too sluggish and insensitive; and merits no description.

Reproduction of sound from a developed film, or from a positive print of that negative, is now accomplished by a photoelectric cell. This device, commonly known as an "electrical eye", was discovered before its present-day explanation in terms of electrons became possible. In its simplest form it is a small glass bulb, rather completely evacuated and containing for one electrode a short length of wire. The inner surface of the bulb, except for a portion of one side through which the controlling light is to enter, is coated with some metal like caesium or potassium. The metallic coating is the other electrode of the cell. When light falls on the coating, electrons are emitted from it in a number proportional to the intensity of the light. If a battery is connected so as to make the wire electrode positive and the coating negative the electrons will be drawn to the wire as fast as they are freed by the light.

This action is identical with that in the filament-plate circuit of a vacuum tube as described on page 100, except that electrons are emitted by light instead of by heat. The current derived from the cell has a value at all times accurately proportional to the amount of light which enters. This current may be amplified in the usual way by vacuum tubes.

When the photoelectric cell is used in reproducing sound from film records it may be thought of as taking the place of the eye in scanning the imaginary molecular ribbon of the earlier discussion. The light which reaches it depends upon the molecular congestion; and hence the current, being proportional to the light, will follow the time pattern of the acoustic pressure. In practice, of course, the photoelectric cell does not view the actual molecules which take part in the sound wave but instead their equivalent in the photographic density of the film. In that way a current is obtained which involves the same variations as existed in the microphone current occasioned by the original sound.

The photoelectric cell and the same arrangement of apparatus [1] serves also to reproduce from variable area sound tracks.

For motion pictures, sound starts on the set in the studio and ends days later at the theater in synchronism with the action projected on the screen. In radio broad-

---

[1] A discussion of sound recording and its apparatus from a different point of view is given in "Signals and Speech", Chapter XII.

casting, transmission from studio to audience is practically instantaneous. In the pictures, the current variations produced by the microphone are recorded; the continuity of telephonic transmission is thereby broken and a delay introduced. Hours, or days, later a duplicate of the record originates a reproduction of the current which continues the journey to its destination in the loudspeaker behind the curtain of a theater.

In straight transmission the quality of the reproduced sound is dependent primarily upon the terminal apparatus, microphone and loudspeaker, with due allowances for the acoustics of studio and auditorium. The processes of recording and reproducing introduce two additional sources of possible distortion. Therefore, it is sometimes difficult, when there is poor quality, to assign the blame to the proper part of an entire electro-acoustical system or to the human beings upon whose judgment and skill the adjustments of the various parts depend. Two producers using apparatus common in design and manufacture may differ widely in their results. Theaters will show pronounced differences among themselves due in part to acoustic conditions. It is for that reason that the comparison of systems and apparatus requires usually many carefully obtained experimental data as well as trained judgment and wide experience. Economic and engineering factors must also be taken into account.

Only the most general indications of the range and possibilities of various commercial systems will, therefore, be attempted in this book. And nothing which is written should be understood as favoring one system more than another.

Lateral-cut phonograph discs can record sound from about 40 to about 5500 cycles with a characteristic that is practically flat from 300 to 5500 but droops for the lower frequencies and is down about 15 db at 40 cycles. This reduction of efficiency in recording is deliberate and is due to the fact that the amplitude of the waves of a low-frequency tone will be greater than that of a high-frequency tone of equal acoustic power. The low-frequency tones, therefore, are discriminated against for the very practical reason that otherwise the waves in one spiral on the disc might overlap and cut into those in an adjacent spiral. At the upper frequencies, also, in the usual commercial record the characteristic is sloped down from about 4000 cycles; and very little is recorded or reproduced above 4500. This is due to the practice of mixing an abrasive with the material of the disc so as to "grind in" the needle of the reproducer. The result is the reproduction of "needle scratch" which appears as a "background noise" in phonograph playing. It is most noticeable in the silent portions of a record but is not so obvious in other portions because it is down about 30 db from the music. It is made less obvious by penalizing all the higher frequencies—but the penalty is imposed, of course, upon scratch and music alike.

Vertical-cut phonograph discs of the most recent type can record from 40 to 9000 cycles. Below 300 cycles there is electrical compensation which results in a practically flat characteristic. Scratch noise is reduced more than a hundred times, and these records can preserve a range of intensities of 50 or more db. They were used to record not only speech and music but some of the complex currents which were necessary for the demonstration of telephone apparatus at the first "Century of Progress" Exposition. They are used for radio transcriptions and for music distribution systems in hotels, parks and amusement centers. The incidental music in the Bell System Exhibit at the San Diego Exposition of 1935 was derived from such records.

Film recording, whether variable area or variable density, has its own problems of background noise. In both systems it has been reduced by specially designed equipment so that today the loudspeakers of a well-equipped motion-picture theater emit little noise during the silent portions of a film. The background noise is down about 45 db from the peaks of music. The frequency range is practically a little less than that of vertically-cut records. The loudness range is about 45 db. This is appreciably more than radio broadcasting can handle. It is insufficient for the faithful reproduction of the intensity range of a fair sized orchestra, which is about 50 db, and more inadequate for a large orchestra, for which the crescendo may be 70 db above its pianissimo passages. This subject of range of intensities, however, ties in with that of "Noise" and will be discussed in a later chapter of that title.

All the methods of sound recording which have been described in this chapter are in commercial use in the United States. For home use the phonograph records are of the lateral-cut type; the vertical-cut records must run at a different speed and are not adaptable to the same turntables; they are in use in Western Electric sound-distribution systems. In the motion-picture industry the flashing-light method for variable-density

recording on film is illustrated by news reels of Movie-
tonews Inc., although this company also uses the light
valve; the variable area by those of the affiliates of the
Radio Corporation of America; and the variable density records, made with a light valve. are those of the
several producers licensed by Electrical Research Products, Inc., to use Western Electric sound systems.

12

A roaring lion, according to the best published data, establishes a noise level of 87 decibels about eighteen feet away. He raises his voice about five hundred million times above the threshold of audibility. The level for a Bengal tiger is down about ten decibels from the lion; and that for a barking dog another ten or fifteen.

"Thunder" which used to be the accepted term for a loud noise has just about the noise level, when its lightning source is a mile or more away, of a barking dog at twenty feet. The undertone of street noise in a large city is about 45 db, and it rises to 75 or 80 as rattling trucks, street cars or elevated trains pass by and add their special noises. Below 45 but above 20 is the range for residences when the windows are closed. Office and other non-residential buildings have their noise levels between 30 and 70 db.

Among outdoor noises the most common, and one of the most severe, is that of the automobile horn. The average level, as determined by measurements on 34 different types, is above 90 db at a point seven or eight paces in front of the horn. This is an average figure, the maximum is above 100 db. Pneumatic riveting and hammering on steel plates exceed the automobile horn by the ten or so added decibels that make the sound painful if its source is only a few feet away.

The average city dweller lives in an atmosphere of

noise which is practically always 30 db above his threshold of audibility, unless he shuts the windows and pulls
the blankets over his head, and for most of his working
day is never less than 50 but may rise intermittently
to 90 or higher. He is subjected to a louder and more
continuous noise than the primitive man from whom
he inherits his nervous system. How much he is affected
thereby has not yet been adequately determined but
enough is known to make "noise abatement" a socially
desirable project.

An obvious objection to noise is its masking of the
sounds one would like to hear. Its amount can be expressed in terms of its masking effect and some of the
earliest reliable measurements were based on that principle. An instrument had been constructed, for use in
telephonic researches on the sensitivity of hearing,
which permitted rapid measurement of the thresholds
of audibility for each of several pure tones an octave
apart. This audiometer consisted of a vacuum-tube oscillator, which generated a sinusoidal current of a specified
frequency when the proper switch was thrown, a dial-
controlled potentiometer for adjusting the intensity of
the current and a head receiver. Turning the dial one
way weakened the current progressively until it was
below the threshold of audibility of the listener and the
other way raised it. The dial position as read on a calibrated scale gave the number of decibels below a convenient reference level.

To use this audiometer as a noise-measuring instrument an observer first determined with it the levels of
his own threshold for the different tones. Then he sub-
stituted a telephone receiver which had a large opening

in its side so that it no longer protected the listening ear from extraneous sounds. Taking the apparatus to the place where the noise was to be measured, he repeated the determination of his own thresholds for the tones which the audiometer produced. Because of the masking effect he would have to supply to his ear a much more intense tone before it could be perceived. In effect his entire threshold was raised, exactly as if he had suffered partial deafening. The difference in level between his normal and the raised threshold, expressed in decibels, was a quantitative statement of the intensity of the noise so far as concerned its interference with audition.

That extraneous noise raises the threshold of audibility explains the well known fact that those who are partially deaf appear to hear better when there is considerable noise. Noise which is easily perceptible to one of normal hearing may be below the threshold for one who is deficient. To the one of normal hearing the noise may be completely masking unless the speech or music which he is trying to hear is correspondingly more intense than it would normally have to be. When the noise is so great that the normal ear can only just perceive a sound which is loud enough to be perceptible to the deficient ear there is for the moment no effective difference between them. All conversation then must be carried on in loud tones or in shouts; and no one expects to be heard if he drops his voice to an ordinary level. Under those conditions the person who is partially deaf is at no disadvantage.

The noise levels which were cited at the beginning of this chapter, more of which are tabulated on page

244, were not determined by their masking effect. Instead they were obtained by portable apparatus embodying some of the principles of the apparatus used in measuring peak and average power of musical instruments. The equipment measured average power during intervals of two-tenths of a second; and also it determined the proportion of the noise in three frequency regions, 250-750, 750-1500 and 1500-5600 cycles. Although noises differ, of course, in their frequency spectra it has been found that the masking effects are similar for most of the sounds which constitute out-of-door noise in a city. There is a fairly constant difference between the level of the noise and the deafening effect. The difference is about 15 decibels. This means, for example, that a person standing on the corner of 42nd Street and Fifth Avenue in New York City, where in business hours the noise level fluctuates between 60 and 75 db, is for the moment just as badly off in audition as a person of defective hearing whose threshold in the middle range of frequencies is 45 to 60 db above normal. He has lost 25 to 35 percent of normal hearing.

Whenever sounds are to be perceived they must be above the level of surrounding noise. That is a most obvious idea. No component in a complex sound must be allowed to fall in intensity below the noise level if its perception is desired. There is no recovery; once a component has slipped into the undertone of noise it is sunk forever. Amplification is then unavailing for it magnifies impartially both the noise, with which the lapsing component is irretrievably associated, and the remaining components, which have kept above the noise level.

Music, speech, or signal, whatever is to be transmitted must start appreciably above the noise level and never be allowed to sink below. In engineering terms, the signal-to-noise ratio must exceed some minimum if the intelligibility of the signal is not to suffer.

In electrical communication the signal is constituted by the components of a complex alternating current. All other currents which may be present in the transmission line are "noise currents" to the communication engineer. They will have their effect when they reach the receiving equipment; and they may mask the signal. The rule, therefore, is to keep large the ratio of signal currents to noise.

There are two ways to make a ratio large; one is to increase the numerator, in this case the signal; and the other is to decrease the denominator, the noise. When one tries to talk to a friend on a noisy thoroughfare he instinctively keeps close and talks loud. If he is in a noisy restaurant he knows that he must lean closer to the ear he would reach. If he is broadcasting he speaks right into the microphone, making the ratio of his signal large as compared to the noise which accompanies it, and in addition he profits by the sound-proof protection of the studio which decreases the denominator of the ratio.

The signal-noise ratio must be large at the start. Imagine, for concrete cases, that one speaks into a microphone in an atmosphere of noise at 30 db. If his intensity level is 20 to 30 db higher some of his consonants are just dangling in the noise. The weaker ones are submerged. Reproduce that speech electrically as loud as is desired and the noise rises with the speech.

In the pauses the noise is more than noticeable; and during the feebler sounds it is annoying or completely masking. On the other hand, let the average level of the speech be 40 db above the noise; then, not only is none of it masked but it stands out clearly above. In fact, a listener is hardly conscious of a background of noise except during complete pauses when his attention is not held by the louder and more interesting sound.

Assuming that the signal-noise ratio is sufficiently large in the input to a transmitter there remains for the communication engineer the problem of preventing any increase of noise during transmission. He shields and protects his lines to prevent them from inductively picking up irrelevant currents from neighboring circuits. This is sometimes an almost meticulous task and correspondingly expensive. For the program circuits which the telephone company provides to connect studios and broadcasting stations the engineers arrange that the noise currents shall be 40 to 50 db below the maximum signal current.

When the current arrives at its destination the noise level with which the loudspeaker must contend becomes of importance. If the room is noisy the ratio of the loudspeaker's output to the surrounding noise may be too low—if not for those closest to the speaker, nevertheless for those farthest away, since the level of the signal falls six decibels every time the distance is doubled.

In pick-up, in transmission and in reproduction the signal must never be below the noise level. The noise, or noise current, sets the lower level to which the signal should be allowed to fall. The upper level is set by the characteristics of the various elements in the system. The speech or music, whether in acoustic or electrical form, must never be so intense as to overload either the transmitter, or the loudspeaker or any intervening amplifier, because then distortion will be introduced. Instead of clear music with a few well defined tones there will be a "mush" of tone, with all the harmonics and components of cross modulation which were described in Chapter 8.

Between this devil of distortion and the deep sea of noise there must take place all transmission if sound is to be reproduced with fidelity. In radio the lower level is usually set by static, the heaven-sent radio signals which crack and sizzle in a receiver. The upper level is overloading in the vacuum tubes, usually of the home receiving set; and in its loudspeaker. The difference between these levels is about 30 db. Equipment could be designed for a wider range but the cost would be higher and in the case of most receiving sets the space occupied also might have to be increased.

In recording equipment the range lies between the lower limit of background noise and an upper limit which is usually some form of overloading. In disc records one limit is that of over-cutting so that waves in adjacent turns overlap. In film recording it may be set by the danger of clashing, or of overtravel by the light valve ribbons or the oscillographic vibrator. For lateral-cut disc records the range is about 35 db. For either variable-area or variable-density records on film it is about the same. For vertical-cut disc records the range is about 45 db. In the all-wire circuit used in the Philadelphia-Washington transmission, which was described in earlier chapters, the range was 75 db; but that requires expensive construction and many refinements of design and operation. The best grade of program circuit will transmit a range of 40 to 50 db, so much more than the radio stations broadcast that it adds no limitations.

As a convenient figure to carry in mind one is not far wrong in taking 30 db as the intensity range within which must be compressed most of the music which is electrically disseminated. When that figure is compared to the intensity ranges of symphony orchestras, small and large, or even to that of good old-fashioned stage ranting, it is apparent that it is inadequate. Dance orchestras, on the other hand, the music of which forms such a large part of radio programs, do not cover so large a volume range. Their music is well within the 30 db limits and presents no serious problems.

In the electrical transmission of music, at some point between the microphone and the equipment for broadcasting, or recording as the case may be, there are dials to control the amplification of the music-bearing currents. In effect these are like the volume control dial on a radio receiving set which regulates the amplification of the current en route to the loudspeaker. In radio or sound picture equipment the controls are associated with a "volume indicator", which is a meter to indicate continuously the average intensity of the currents. It indicates by the position of its pointer what the average current has been over the preceding fraction of a second. In some types of volume indicator this fraction is 0.2 second but it might be less.

The volume indicator guides the technical operator in his task of keeping the sound-bearing currents within the proper range for the system of equipment for which they are supplied. He should keep them above the lower, or noise, limit and below the upper, or overload, limit. In most cases that range is 30 db. In order that the operation shall always be as far as possible above the noise limit he arranges that the currents for the louder parts of the program shall be amplified to about the upper limit. And his problem comes when successive crescendos occur in the music. He is already up and has nowhere to go. If he is caught off his guard he can only turn the dial to reduce the input and prevent serious distortion and perhaps dangerous overloading. But he is rarely off his guard because rehearsals, experience and musical judgment prepare him for the sustained peaks of power. As one approaches he backs off, reducing the intensity and in general submerging the weaker tones in the undercurrent of noise; but he has prepared his equipment for sharp increases. And then he lets them go into the levels where distortion occurs, but not so far as to overload with danger to the equipment. When the music demands more than the 30 db range that the electro-acoustical system allows, he deliberately lets it down a few db into the noise and permits it to rise a few db into the region of distortion; and so he is able to stand a range about 10 db larger, a total of 40 instead of 30.

For sound picture and phonograph recording the intensity of the sound-bearing currents is controlled in the same general manner as for radio. Under the best of conditions, the recording and reproducing systems will handle a range of 40 to 45 db. That is not quite enough to meet the range of a small orchestra which is about 50 db and much less than the 70 db of the large orchestra.

Express these ratios in figures and the requirements are startling. Orchestras have ranges of power between their pianissimo and fortissimo of 100,000/1 to 10,000,000/1. Vertical recording will handle about 30,000/1; film recording about 30,000/1; radio, by some jugglery, 10,000/1; but with its most perfect quality only about 1000/1. The extremes of loudness are inadequately reproduced; but again the ear comes to the rescue. Few listeners want a 70-horsepower orchestra let loose in the living rooms of their houses or apartments. Pehaps 30 db is too small—the author thinks 50 is about right—but certainly 70 db is something to leave home for. And when one gets to his seat in the music hall he may not be conscious of such an extreme range because some of the weaker tones may be lost in an undertone of noise, program rustles and snuffles.

Seventy decibels is necessary for reproduction in facsimile. When a perfect facsimile is required the level at which distortion begins must be 10,000,000 times the noise intensity. The human ear can tolerate greater extremes than that; and the music of the future may involve them because suitable electro-acoustical apparatus is available. The upper limit then will be level with the threshold of feeling. The lower limit will always be noise; and except under refined laboratory conditions it will probably be set by the audience itself.

Even under the best of conditions there is one common physical limit beyond which noise cannot be reduced. In electrical transmission it sets a limit below which the currents with significant variations must never fall. It is a phenomenon of the electrons in the conducting wires of the circuit. Within any wire there are billions of electrons scuttling about beneath its apparently solid surface. On the average as many go in one direction as in any other. At any particular instant, however, the condition is rarely that of a statistical balance; the rate at which electrons are shifting toward one end of the wire may be slightly greater than toward the other. At that instant there is effectively a very minute current. Its amount and direction are matters of chance; and change from instant to instant; and its alternations occur with no regularity whatever.

In any electrical circuit there is always such a current flow,[1] a complex of innumerable alternating current components, entirely fortuitous and meaningless in their variations. If amplified sufficiently and translated into variations of air pressure, as by a loudspeaker, it will manifest itself as noise. Due as it is to the thermal agitation of the particles which compose the conductors of any circuit, it is inevitable at all temperatures above the absolute zero. If a signal current is so feeble that its amplitudes are of the same order of magnitude as the amplitudes of this thermal agitation its meaning is obscured. No amplification can then alter the situation. All that can issue from the loudspeaker is a roar like city traffic on cobblestone streets.

From recent considerations it now appears that in

[1] This is the Johnson effect which is discussed in "Natural Limits", Chapter XIV of "Signals and Speech".

the evolution of audition thermal agitation may have set the lower limit. At any rate, the threshold of hearing is only slightly above the level at which the casual and minute, but rapid, motions of the molecules and atoms of the ear itself would produce audible effects. From that we can conclude that the human ear has very nearly the greatest sensitivity which is physically possible. Its physiological and psychological possibilities have not been limited by poor design of its physical structure.

13

The tower of Babel, of itself, was probably not a noisy place; nor was the city which was built around it. From the Biblical reports which have been handed down, it appears that the entire structure must have been poorly designed from the standpoint of acoustics. Its sun-baked bricks, or tiles, would reflect sounds and give rise to conflicting and recurring echoes and reverberations. The acoustics seem to have been so bad that the inhabitants had serious difficulty in understanding each other. When one Shinarian tried to talk to another the ratio of direct to reverberant sound was probably too low at the ear of the listener. A low value to this ratio is much more serious in conversation than it is in the production of music.

Reverberation is the term applied to echoes when they are so numerous and overlapping that they merge their individualities into a single continuous effect. In a room with smooth hard walls sound can undergo reflections and trace paths that would be the envy of a three-cushion billiard player. So complex is the pattern for even a simple rectangular room with reflecting floor and ceiling that it is easier to study the gross effect.

Imagine in the room which is to be studied a source of sustained pure tone and an ear, human or electrical. An instant after the tone starts its direct sound reaches the ear. An instant later there is an addition due to a wave train which arrives by an indirect route after reflection from some boundary surface. Successively such additions are made until all the possible paths are being followed. A steady state is thus reached which is maintained as long as the source operates.

The sound intensity at the ear is the sum of a large number of contributions from sources which are conveniently to be considered as images of the real source, by analogy with optical images. Imagine standing near a mirror in front of which is a lamp. One is then illuminated by the direct rays from the lamp and by the reflected rays. The reflected light appears to the eye to come from the image of the lamp in the mirror. All the effects will be exactly the same if no mirror is present but instead another lamp is located where the real lamp has its mirror image. This second lamp will not be as powerful as the first because of the loss by absorption at the mirror surface. Its light travels a longer path than the direct beam and takes correspondingly longer to do so.

If several mirrors reflect back and forth the light from a single lamp the effect is the same as if there were no mirrors, but instead a lamp source of proper strength for each of the various mirror images of the original lamp. When the original lamp is extinguished all the images go out, but their contributions to the total of illumination are not discontinued until the last bit of light they emit, as they expire, has traveled its path.

Mirrors and reflecting surfaces diffuse the light from a single source, spreading it through space and producing at each point a total of illumination which is effectively that of a large number of scattered sources. The corresponding effect in acoustics is reverberation.

When a source of sound in a reverberant room ceases to radiate its various mirror images also cease and the acoustic intensity at each point falls off at a rate which depends upon the distances to the various images and upon their respective powers. It decreases at a rate which the mathematicians describe as logarithmic. Only direct illumination can fail sharply, and also only direct sound; diffused light and reverberant sound decay in the manner the mathematicians describe. But all they mean is that the intensity drops the same number of decibels in each succeeding instant of time.

The time required for a sound to fall down sixty decibel steps is the convenient measure for the acoustic condition of an auditorium or a studio. The importance of this "reverberation time" was first appreciated by the late Professor W. C. Sabine of Harvard, who did much early work in developing scientific techniques for the problems of auditorium acoustics. In his day there was no system of vacuum-tube oscillator, amplifier, and loudspeaker for producing a steady single-frequency tone; and organ pipes were used. There was no combination of electrical ear, intensity meter and recording mechanism; and stop watches or chronographs were used to time the decay until the sound of the pipe fell to the threshold of audibility and ceased to be heard. Today these measurements are made automatically by refined equipment which gives a continuous graphic record of the intensity of the sound as it decays, and so presents very accurate data for the determination of the reverberation time.

Reverberation occurs only in enclosed or partially enclosed spaces. Imagine a musician playing out of doors: the sound he creates suffers no reflection and never returns. Now imagine him in a room before a large open window. The sound which passes through the window is lost into space. Of that which strikes the walls some is reflected; and some is absorbed and has its energy dissipated. The window, as W. C. Sabine reasoned, represents complete absorption over its entire area and the walls fractions of that completeness depending upon the materials and character of their construction. The less absorbing are the walls of a room, the greater the reflection and the longer the time that sound "hangs on." A cocktail party on the screened porch is never as noisy as one in the living room.

Large rooms, other things being equal, have larger reverberation times. That should seem reasonable because it is only when sound strikes the walls that absorption can occur. If sound, bouncing between floor and ceiling, must strike each five times before it is reduced by 60 db it obviously lasts longer in the higher room.

These two physical magnitudes for a room, namely, its volume and the area of a window, which would be equivalent in absorption to the total area of its walls, determine the time of reverberation. The quantitative relationship was the classic research of Sabine.

If reverberation time is measured for a room with an open window and then again with the window covered by some building material the relative absorption can be calculated from the increase in the time. In that way physical constants can be obtained, as Sabine did, describing various materials. Calling the absorption unity for a given area into open space, the absorption of an equal area of brick wall is only 0.017; and a plastered wall from 0.022 to 0.056 or even higher depending upon whether it is on wood or metal lath and of smooth or rough finish. Obviously these materials are reflecting rather than absorbing.

Heavy velour draperies hung a few inches from a wall have a coefficient as high as 0.45; in other words 100 square feet of such drapery will correspond in absorption to a window opening of 45 square feet. A thick felt of cattle hair has a coefficient of 0.56; a triple Celotex as high as 0.84, about the same as special tile construction with rock-wool fillers. Wood paneling, despite the popular feeling that it is the desirable finish for an auditorium, has an absorption coefficient only one-tenth that of free space.

By selecting the materials of its boundary surfaces there is some control over the reverberation time of a room. The walls, floor, and ceiling, however, do not present the only surfaces from which reflection can take place or at which absorption can occur. All the furniture in the room adds its part. An auditorium chair, with seat and back of veneer, is as effective as a quarter of a square foot of window opening in reducing reverberation time. A theater seat of imitation leather is equivalent to 1.6 square feet of window; and well upholstered in mohair it may be equivalent to as much as 3.0 square feet. What is in a room is more important, therefore, than its walls in determining how "live" or reverberant it is. In the Chicago Civic Opera House the seats supply forty per cent of the sound absorption —neglecting the audience.

An audience contributes about 4.6 square feet of absorbing area per person, according to P. E. Sabine of the Riverbank Laboratories. This is gross, not net. If the audience is seated in chairs which by themselves would absorb like 2.6 square feet the total for chair and occupant is 4.6. The reverberation time for an auditorium varies with the size of the audience. In a large hall like that of the Chicago Opera House a full audience may increase by fifty per cent the entire absorptive capacity. Whereas the reverberation time is 2.93 seconds in the empty hall, when one-third full it becomes 2.51; two-thirds 2.19; and for the maximum audience of 3600 persons 1.95 seconds.

Just what should be the reverberation time for an auditorium is a matter in part of musical taste and judgment and in part of tradition. Habit and tradition associate organ music, for example, with churches and cathedrals where reflection is high and reverberation pronounced. In Bayreuth Wagnerian music is produced in a highly reverberant theater; Italian opera, on the other hand, has become associated with its reverberation in continental opera houses which have tiers of balconies and boxes. These have shorter reverberation times, because boxes, for example, act like open windows through which the music passes without returning; it is absorbed in the heavy hangings. These opera houses are also relatively small for the size of their audiences; and smaller halls under equal conditions have less reverberation.

Among auditoriums generally credited as being acoustically good, the reverberation times, with full audiences, run from 1.44 for Symphony Hall in Detroit,

1.75 and 1.76 respectively for Carnegie Hall in New York and the Academy of Music in Philadelphia, 1.90 for the Auditorium in Chicago, to 1.93 for Symphony Hall in Boston.

A reverberation time of two seconds means approximately that an orchestral strain, produced with full volume, does not die out completely to an acute listener until that time after the performers have finished its production. Reverberation prolongs and enhances musical notes, increasing the overlapping of one tone upon another. For certain kinds of music that is desired; in part, because the direct sound, itself, would not satisfy the listener; it needs to be built up by successive reflections and sustained thereby. A string quartette or a vocal soloist is at a disadvantage when there is no reverberation. On the other hand, whether by tradition or otherwise, a band seems more mellow in the open air where its sounds are quickly dissipated and only the direct sound reaches the listener.

Musicians as a rule have made little effort to correlate their judgments with physical magnitudes and thus lay a scientific basis on which engineers and designers can construct better music halls and studios. One difficulty of a practical nature is the dual use of halls for instrumental music and public speeches. A hangover of sound which might be pleasant in one case would be destructive in the other. A reverberation time greater than two seconds interferes appreciably with the interpretation of speech. It forces the listener to rely on context to understand syllables which have been distorted by overlapping waves of earlier syllables. The effect is reported by Knudsen to be noticeable in loss of articulation for a time as low as one second. Speech must be slower in a large reverberant hall to be easily intelligible.

On the other hand, for there is no law, merely taste and preference, if a room is too highly damped, has too small a reverberation time, it is correctly called "dead" because music in it seems dull and lifeless; and speech, although distinct, is thin and lacks volume.

The present tendency is probably toward shorter reverberation times than were accepted or tolerated a generation or two ago. When bricks, stone and plaster and wood, glass and metal were the materials available to builders of cathedrals large reverberation times were inevitable and, like oxtail soup among exigent Huguenots, may for that reason have been accepted. During the last twenty years, however, many new materials have been developed that permit acoustic treatment of all sizes of rooms.

Another influence is the development of public address systems—one-way telephone systems with amplifiers and loudspeakers—whereby enormous audiences may be reached. Through their use even the cathedral type of auditorium with its transepts may be adapted to the spoken word. So skilfully can microphone and loudspeaker be located that listeners close to the speaker may be unable to tell whether they are hearing direct or reproduced sound. Through their use the intensity of the speech is increased hundreds of thousands of times. This greater intensity means a longer time before the sound dies out. For example, in a hall of reverberation time two seconds, speech 60 db above audibility will be inaudible two seconds later; but speech 90 db above will require three seconds. The use of electrical equipment for reproducing sound requires therefore smaller reverberation if the "acoustics" is to remain as good as before.

Except when such equipment is to be used, a safe rule for reverberation time is to keep it between one and two seconds, in the lower part of that range for speech and for the electrical reproduction of speech and music as in a motion-picture theater.

In studios where motion pictures are produced, or phonograph records made, and in the studios from which radio programs are broadcast new problems of acoustics have arisen which are not yet completely solved. In all those cases a microphone picks up the sound in the studio and a loudspeaker reproduces it in home or theater. The listeners can hear only what the microphone has heard. It does not hear what a visitor to the studio would hear for the simple reason that the latter listens with two ears while the microphone is a single electrical ear.

Listening binaurally one can discriminate between sounds according to their direction, at least to the extent of partial exclusion of sounds from undesired sources. Monaurally one has no auditory perspective and the only evidence for judging the distance away of a sound source is the ratio of the direct sound to the reverberant. Coordinating that ratio with the visual perspective enhances the illusion in talking-motion pictures, where the recording system is not only one-eared but has only one eye. The reverberation time of the sound picture set, it is reported, should be only about three-fourths that for the same size of room when used by an audience. The binaural ability to distinguish to some extent between direct sound and undirected reverberation allows more reverberation than should be recorded for reproduction. When reproduced, both the direct sound and the reverberation, which originally accompanied it, issue from the same loudspeaker; and the binaural audition of the audience availeth not.

In phonograph recording and in broadcasting another question is of importance: Shall a listener to a radio set be in effect a listener at a window into the auditorium of the original performance? Shall he hear what he might if he sat in an orchestra seat but could listen with only one ear because the other was unannoyingly plugged with cotton? In that case he hears not only the direct sound but all the reverberation which is natural to the particular auditorium. The question, however, needs some elaboration because the listener is not in an orchestra seat. He is in his own living room with its individual acoustics. From a panel in a corner of that room there issues in amplified form —except as subject to the limitations of present-day radio in matters of frequency band and intensity range —the complex of sound that would have fallen upon his ear. If that is to be the character of the reproduced music the microphone which picks it up is not just a few inches from the mouth of the soloist or on the conductor's stand. It is out in front, over the audience, but not so far away as to pick up much of the audience noise.

The other extreme may be pictured in terms of a window into the living room which is concealed by the radio set. Out-of-doors in front of the window stands the soloist. He sings into space and there are no re-verberations. His studio is completely dead. That is the sound which the radio listener then hears. Because it is unaccompanied by reverberation it is more direct and more intimate. For that reason this condition is much preferred by those who listen to crooners; while those who listen to orchestras or political speech probably prefer a fair amount of reverberation on the basis of which they can reproduce in imagination the original situation. Some records, for example, of the Philadelphia Symphony Orchestra, playing in an empty Academy of Music, have been highly approved although the reverberation is noticeable because the time for the empty hall is 2.3 seconds as against 1.76 with a full audience.

Present-day practice in radio studios seems to be away from the very dead studios of the early days and to tend toward the reverberation times of audience rooms of similar sizes. From time to time experiments are carried out in which listeners are asked to participate but so far insufficient data are available for final conclusions. The range of possible judgments is also large and personal prejudices as to types of program have large effects. Certainly the amount of reverberation, or more strictly the ratio of direct to reverberant sound which depends upon the placement of the microphone with reference to the source, should be different for different types of programs. For some an illusion of the actual situation is desirable and for others the illusion of intimacy. This is not difficult for the speaker who will set his voice at the level for discussion in a small group but presents a different problem to the concert or stage singer who must set his at a crooning level. In both cases there enters another difficulty. Unnatural effects are produced when voices pitched for one type of audience are electrically reproduced at markedly higher levels.

Reverberation despite its esthetic value is a distortion, one of the two which take place when sound energy is confined by walls. Not only do the reflecting boundaries introduce additions to the direct sound when it starts and so require a longer time before the steady state is reached, and similarly delay its decay; but also they produce distortions which vary in their characteristics from point to point throughout the enclosed space.

If two waves of the same pure tone arrive at a point along different paths their resultant effect will depend upon their relative phases. If, for example, one wave train should demand that the molecule of air at that point move in one direction while the other train demands a diametrically opposite motion, the resultant oscillation of the molecule must be less than either train would produce by itself. Under equal urges, of course, there would be complete interference and no motion at all. Since the wave trains have the same frequency they continue to neutralize each other's effect as long as their sources continue to act. At some other point, however, their phases may be such that they add. When a steady tone is sustained in a hall, points can usually be found where the sound is less and others where it is greater. If the frequency of the source is changed this interference pattern is altered and neutralization occurs at other locations.

Because of such interference the sound of a pure tone in an auditorium does not decay with perfect smoothness. It may happen, for example, that at the point where the measurement is being made waves from two of the image sources are in interference. When radiation from one of these ceases, that from the other is no longer neutralized, with the result that the total reverberant sound is larger than it was the instant before.

When music is being played there are present waves of many different frequencies. And for each frequency there is a different interference pattern. At fairly nearby points in an auditorium, therefore, the music is different and its notes die out in slightly different manners. One does not hear from his seat exactly the same music as others even in the same section of the hall.

Perhaps you are reading this chapter by artificial light. Even under the best of conditions light is not uniformly distributed and areas equally distant from the source are not equally illuminated. A quick glance around a room will tell whether or not that is so. In the sweep of the eye a comparison is made of the brightness of similar surfaces. So natural is such a judgment that if one picks up a book in an irregularly lighted room he instinctively turns or moves to a position of more adequate illumination.

An ocular comparison of this character is possible only when the intensity of the radiation from the lamp remains constant during the series of observations. You cannot be sure that one corner of a room is darker than another if, while you turn from one to the other, the light source changes in brilliancy. It is also necessary for accurate judgment that the surfaces which are compared shall be similar in texture and color and in the angle at which they reflect to the observer.

Instead of light let there be a source of sound. It is now impossible from a single position to draw any conclusion whatever as to the distribution of the sound. The only way a comparison can be made is by placing one's ear successively at the locations which are to be compared. Since this is awkward and a human ear is not a good measuring instrument for a series of determinations of acoustic power, it is usual to employ an electrical ear. A microphone can be mounted on an arm, or boom, to swing around the source of sound; and the current can be recorded continuously as its position changes. In that way the sound intensity can be obtained for each angular degree around the circle.

Such data are presented most conveniently in what is known as a polar plot. On a sheet of paper place a dot and radially from it draw lines in every direction. Give to each line a length proportional to the intensity. of the sound in that direction. Usually the interest is in only half the possible directions, namely those within 90 degrees on either side of the direction in which the sound source faces. If it radiates uniformly over this 180 degrees the plot will be half of a circle; but generally the graph resembles a leaf of a plant, as does that shown on page 259 for the sound from a violin.

If a blindfolded and one-eared listener were swung slowly around a semicircle with a violinist at its center he would probably insist that he was being moved back and forth from the source. Without eyes to aid, and without the ability to judge direction which is the important phenomenon of binaural audition, changes in intensity must be associated with changes of distance. When this hypothetical listener is in the position to face directly the violin—not the violinist—the sound he receives may be as much as 9 db above the intensity he will receive in most of the other possible positions.

This directivity for the music of a violin may be pictured in terms of an audience. Arrange twenty chairs on a semicircle of twenty foot radius about a violinist. One or two of the occupants will get 8 or 10 times more acoustic power than the others. This is upon the assumption, of course, that the test takes place in a dead room so that the listeners receive only direct and not reverberant sound. It is also upon the assumption that the musician and his instrument are fixed in position. When he changes position the pattern rotates. If he turns and sways he'll wobble it a little so that the maximum will fall sometimes on those on either side of the favored position. Six or eight members of the semi-circle may thus be in line to receive an amount of acoustic power which varies with the position of the instrument. For the others in the group the intensity will not change much, according to the plot on page 259. No member of the group has any immediate basis for the comparison of what he hears with that which others hear. Even when the direction of maximum intensity swings right and left through his position it is doubtful if he can appreciate the existence of those variations. The notes are not sustained for a long enough time to permit the variation in intensity to be detected; or, otherwise expressed, the variations are not rapid enough to be noted. If they occurred periodically two or three times a second they would be most easily recognized.

The variations, however, are there; and they may amount to as much as one-third the intensity range which radio usually handles. They follow the varying position of the violin. Are such swings of position an effort of a violinist to correct for the sharply directional characteristics of his music? Similar variations occur, of course, in instruments of the same family, like the cello, which are usually held firmly in one position while being played. Or, are they a necessary part of the technique for a violin? or a traditional or temperamental necessity? Conversely, are the variations in power to which a listener's ear is exposed, while a violinist is maintaining a constant intensity, esthetically essential?

The answers to questions of this kind have a definite bearing on the electrical music of the future. For example, imagine the violinist to face a battery of microphones, so arranged that their combined output is always the maximum power of his instrument regardless of his changing position. Now translate the current through a loudspeaker which will distribute the sound with practical uniformity in all directions. No one in the audience of the loudspeaker is then subjected to partiality; and all hear exactly what the violinist plays. Is that a result which music lovers would approve? On the other hand, if variations in intensity are desired the electrical equipment can be controlled to introduce them as often as wished and of any preferred magnitude. Considerable research may be required to answer these questions and to correlate variability with esthetics. The necessary tools, however, are available whenever musicians and engineers wish to cooperate in such investigations and have the funds.

A properly designed loudspeaker—it may be one of several elements and channels—can distribute music through a hall so that the direct sound is the same for all listeners at the same distance from the speaker. There are obvious box-office advantages to a system which can deliver to all seats alike; but there is another aspect to be considered.

What a loudspeaker can deliver so impartially must first be collected by a microphone. This electrical ear picks up the same sound as would a one-eared listener in its place. When the source of sound is a soloist, microphone and monaural listener are at no disadvantage as compared to a binaural observer. This is true also, of course, whenever the music arises from a group of sources, as for example a band, provided it is far enough away. For an orchestra in an ordinary auditorium, where the instruments are distributed throughout a considerable angle, the binaural listener has the advantage. He can detect the direction of the individual sources.

Aural localization of the direction from which a sound comes has its physical basis in the different effects which the wave produces in the two ears. One of the obvious differences, but one usually of least importance, is in the time of arrival of the wave at the opposite ears. When one hears a short sharp sound, like a tick or click, he tends instinctively to turn toward the side on which it was heard first.

Another difference, which is particularly important when the sound is complex, is that of quality. The high-frequency components of a sound are propagated in short waves. For example, at ordinary room temperature the wave length of a pure tone of 1134 cycles is one foot; of 2268 cycles, six inches, which is about the shortest distance between ears, and of 8000 cycles, a component of some speech sibilants, only one and three-quarter inches. Whether or not a wave train casts a sharp shadow depends upon the size of the obstacle as compared to the wave length. Just as a pin point will form a shadow to a light, so objects as small as the human features will shade from a radiation of high-pitched sound. Listen to speech with one ear and notice how much more pronounced are the consonantal sounds when the speaker faces the ear and the short waves have direct access to the canal. Because of such effects, when one listens binaurally to complex sounds from elsewhere than directly ahead, or behind, the overtone quality is bound to be different at the two ears.

For the middle range of audible frequencies, for which the wave lengths are larger and the shielding can never be complete, the head itself will shield enough to make appreciable difference in loudness at the two ears. Imagine an observer, with his left ear plugged, while a source of steady sound swings around his right side from directly in front to exactly behind. The loudness increases until the source is almost opposite the right ear; then drops; about three-quarters of the way around it falls slightly below the value it had when the source was straight ahead. When the experiment is tried by stopping the right ear instead of the left, but moving the source as before, the loudness decreases more rapidly because the head then acts as a shield. It reaches a minimum when the source is about opposite the right ear and gradually increases, ending at the same value as it did for the right ear.

In binaural hearing each ear functions as just described. The more nearly the sound is directed into one ear, the louder it seems to that ear and more than equally weaker to the other. For speech the difference is as much as 10 db, as shown in the plot on page 261.

When the sound is of low frequency, and is not rich in overtones on the basis of which quality differences may be perceived, its wave length is so large as compared to the human head that there is no shielding and no appreciable difference in loudness. This is particularly true for pure tones below about middle C. In that case the source cannot be located by unaided ears. The sound lacks direction and seems to pervade the surrounding space.

Localization, however, is possible by utilizing a pair of electrical ears with greater separation than is human. Two microphones may be mounted at opposite ends of a long rod, arranged to swing on a pivot at its center. The microphones connect respectively to right and left head-receivers. In the simplest case, the rod with its electrical ears is turned until to the listener the sound seems directly ahead; then the line connecting the microphones will be at right angles to the direction of the sound. This fundamental principle was employed in the World War in the location of airplanes in flight. There is no shielding, however, and the localization is due to the difference in time of arrival of the successive condensations at the two electrical ears. There is, in other words, a difference of phase at the two microphones when the sound arrives obliquely.

Human ears, when sight or the sense of touch also do not supply evidence, can be completely fooled as to direction.[1] Imagine a small stage on which, RU and LU, are two loudspeakers concealed by a front drop. The listener occupies a center seat a few rows back. Current for the speakers comes from a single microphone offstage but the output of each speaker is sepa-

[1] An early illustration was "Oscar" in the exhibit at the 1933 Exposition in Chicago, which is described in the chapter on "Extensions of the Senses" in "Signals and Speech".

rately controlled. A solo artist is before the microphone and the loudspeakers are set for equal volumes. To the listener the soloist is unmistakably just behind the center of the curtain. Next, the output of one speaker is gradually increased, while the other is decreased. The artist apparently is moving behind the curtain toward the more intense speaker. A net difference of about 12 db between loudspeakers will walk him to one side of the stage; and then 24 in the opposite direction will move him to the opposite side.

A more flexible arrangement is obtained when the two loudspeakers are supplied by independent microphones. A portion of the offstage room is then laid out as a miniature or studio stage. On a line in front of this stage, and widely separated, are mounted the microphones. The outputs of the loudspeakers correspond respectively to what the microphones pick up. If a performer on the miniature stage is nearer one microphone than the other, to the listener he will have an acoustical image which will occupy a corresponding position on the curtained stage. As he moves, and so changes the relative proportions which the microphones receive of his acoustic output, his image will move correspondingly. All the sounds on the studio stage are thus reproduced in their spatial relationships.

Through the application of this principle of binaural audition, and by the utilization of high-quality microphones and loudspeakers, it is possible to reproduce with essential illusion an orchestral performance. Somewhat better illusion, as to location front and back, is obtained when three channels are used instead of the two just described. In that case there is provided for the miniature stage a third and centrally-placed micro-phone which is connected to a loudspeaker midway between the other two. This third channel is also particularly advantageous when vocal soloists are to be accompanied by an orchestra.

It was this three-channel system which was used in the first demonstration of transmission and reproduction in auditory perspective, mentioned on page 74. That took place April 27, 1933, under the auspices of the National Academy of Sciences, before whom at an earlier meeting there had been presented a technical discussion of the method and equipment. The demonstration marked the conclusion of a series of telephonic researches in which Dr. Leopold Stokowski and the Philadelphia Orchestra had generously assisted. In Constitution Hall in Washington a large audience of music lovers and scientists listened to the reproduction of a program rendered by the orchestra in Philadelphia under the leadership of Associate Conductor Alexander Smallens. The electro-acoustical system was demonstrated also at Philadelphia, with the orchestra playing in an offstage room; and later in New York City before various engineering societies, with another orchestra.

The original demonstration was certainly an historic occasion from the viewpoint either of music or of electrical communication. Although it was a complete presentation of the new instrumentalities which science had made available to musicians, the emphasis was not upon how the electrons went around but upon the heights to which they could carry a listener. Representative selections from Bach, Beethoven, Debussy and Wagner were interpreted by Dr. Stokowski. For that purpose the dial controls of the electrical equipment were located in a first-row box at the rear of Constitution Hall, from which point he conditioned the music of the distant orchestra to bring it into accord with his own ideal. From the scientific standpoint, however, from which the system must be considered if its potentialities are to be appreciated, the demonstration was not single featured; instead it presented a number of aspects.

First of importance was the fact that the equipment and transmission facilities of each channel picked up, transmitted, and reproduced all the musical sound presented to its microphone which an ordinary human ear could perceive. All components of the music within the range from 40 to 15,000 cycles were faithfully reproduced. Further, there was no compression of the volume range; there was reproduced the full intensity range of the orchestra, a total of 70 db, representing for power of ff as compared to that of pp a ratio of 10,000,000 to 1.

Of similar importance was the arrangement and utilization of three channels whereby the reproduced music was presented in auditory perspective. Not only did this create an illusion, because the instrumental sounds seemed to arise from their usual orchestral positions on the stage, but more importantly it provided the same spreading of music throughout the hall as would have been produced if the orchestra had been present. In that way the "stereophonic" system recreated an atmosphere of sound not perceptibly different from that of a local orchestra. Without that atmosphere, which previous methods of electrical reproduction were unable to provide, music is one dimensional and lacks its true spatial relationships; it lacks in richness and texture.

Through the multichannel system of microphones, lines, amplifiers, and loudspeakers, properly disposed according to the principle of auditory perspective and binaural audition, there may be reproduced in one auditorium all that the ear can perceive of the music which occurs in a distant auditorium. In addition, however, the electrical system was developed and arranged to provide three extensions of music, carrying it beyond its inherent limitations and making possible new artistic effects. These three aspects of the demonstration were completely under the control of Dr. Stokowski who was thus able to produce according to his imagination tonal effects and intensities beyond previous human possibilities, but not necessarily beyond the dreams of composers like Wagner.

The relative importance of these extensions, artistically, may well be a matter of debate. To the present writer who can justify his choice only on the non-artistic basis "I know what I like", it is enough to have heard the finale of Götterdammerung played at full power under Dr. Stokowski's direction; and rising above its most stupendous crescendos, the liquid notes of an unstrained solo voice! The soloist can sing to the central microphone while the other two pick up the orchestra for stereophonic reproduction; and the intensity level of the solo channel can be raised to bring the vocal portion into any desired relationship.

It may well be that the increase of intensity range will ultimately prove to be the extension of greatest importance. Not only can the equipment handle the full 70 db range of a large orchestra but it can transmit and reproduce without overloading, and its consequent distortion, a range of 100 db. Allowing 10 db for the masking of sound by audience noise, this means practically full use of the hearing range of the human ear. Its relationship to the thresholds is shown in the chart on page 251. Because the equipment can provide and tolerate about 20 db more amplification than is needed to reproduce the loudest orchestral music at its original intensity, it becomes possible for a director who controls its dials to increase his orchestra a hundred times. By the turn of a handle he can make its output that of a hundred times as many instruments, but all in the relatively small space required for a normal orchestra. He can also produce musical sounds very close indeed to the threshold of pain!

The last of the three extensions has already been mentioned (on page 77). Dials provide the director with a tapering control for the relative intensities of the components in the music. When he so desires he can enhance all the lower harmonics, emphasizing them the more the lower their frequencies, as pictured in the plot on page 238. Or he may minimize their sounds to an equal degree. For the high-frequency components several steps of control were provided, permitting them to be discriminated against with greater severity. In that way thin tones may be eliminated and an unnatural color given to the music. If the high frequencies are reduced while the low are increased a maximum effect is produced.

What the final judgments on these effects will be, no one knows. Music and art must move slowly for they are deeply rooted in the emotions and traditions. These same controls can, of course, be applied equally well to music other than orchestral, for example, to choir or chorus. Antiphonal effects can be enhanced or imitated by variations of the relative intensities of the right and left channels. Groups of instruments can be emphasized through the central microphone and loudspeaker. And all these, and other effects as yet untried, can be superimposed upon music completely reproduced in all its spatial relationships. The moment—and that moment occurred in the spring of 1933—when it became possible electrically to reproduce all the sounds of orchestral music, there was passed the boundary between natural and electrical music. For better or for worse, we are entering an important new period in the development of music.

"All the lemonade you can drink for a nickel" was the sign over many of the small booths that lined the side of Stony Island Avenue opposite the grounds of the 1893 Columbian Exposition in Chicago. Lemonade was the fancy drink of the day to many middle Westerners; and the advertising appeal was simultaneously to the thirsts of the youngsters and the pocketbooks of their elders. Chemistry was the rising science; and synthetic substitutes, or imitations of natural products, were novelties and sometimes economically profitable.

Synthetic products in the early days of a science or art are likely to be poor substitutes; but as time goes on and technological skill develops, mere imitations cease to be the objective. New products are sought with qualities superior for certain purposes. Today, chemistry, although too frequently the servant of the dishonest manufacturer, is the creator. Its compounds and alloys have affected almost every art, supplying materials better adapted to its needs and encouraging it to revolutionary progress.

Music, however, has been practically unaffected by chemistry except in so far as its products have entered into the equipment of electrical communication. This esthetic art has no reason to fear chemistry; but it should look well to the communication arts, for the music of the future will involve synthetic imitations, substitutes and, very probably, productions superior in various respects to the more natural music of today. Electrical, or synthetic, music is entirely possible.

All the ordinary musical instruments please by virtue of their natural vibrations; and the functions of their performers are to excite these vibrations in the proper order and intensity. When an instrument may produce different tones if played in different manners it is the function of the musician to select and employ the most suitable technique. But, nevertheless and fundamentally, it is the instrument which determines the series of its overtones and their relative importance. By the art of composition and by assemblies of musicians with different musical instruments, complexes of sound may be obtained which have components unlike the overtones of any single instrument either in their intervals above the lowest fundamental or in their relative intensities. It is by such assemblies of the harmonic instruments aided by the less harmonic, like cymbals, that musicians have achieved their most powerful effects.

For any orchestral composition it would be possible, knowing the overtone structure of each instrument and the intensities with which the conductor wished each instrumental note to be played, to express the music in physical terms. A series of pure tones would then replace the orchestral score. Each tone would be defined by its frequency in cycles per second and by its intensity in decibels above or below some reference level. Leave out of account for the moment matters like sliding changes in pitch, the gradual growth of some sounds to their steady state or the sharp attack of others. A series of vacuum-tube oscillators, each controlled in intensity by a dial potentiometer, could produce the music through loudspeakers.

When an orchestra plays in a large hall it may very well happen that the acoustic power—the intensity of the sound—in the audience section of the hall is four or five times as great as the direct sound from the orchestra. That is the result of reverberation. But what it means is that what one hears in a concert hall is not what the orchestra is playing at the moment but the resultant of that and what it played in the preceding two seconds. Four-fifths at least of what the listener hears is sound that has persisted appreciably after its source ceased to function or even after it has produced one or more succeeding notes. When one realizes that fact, one can appreciate the logical conclusion that it is the steady state of radiation which an orchestral instrument produces which affects the listener rather than the short time and transient vibrations which represent the musician's attack. In the piano the attack is most important; and the difficulty of electrical reproduction of a piano does not exist because of the frequency range but because of the short strong components of the sound at the instant it starts. For orchestral music in large halls the attack may not be of great importance per se. Even if it were, by various methods any attack could be electromechanically simulated. The resulting system under keyboard control, and with many of its adjustments automatically performed, could replace an entire orchestra.

Whether it ever does or not, the important point is that the complex music with which composers and conductors deal is physically nothing more than the resultant of a series of pure-tone components of various relative intensities, and of frequencies which are separated by simple ratio intervals.

What is much more probable is that some composer of the future, who understands the electrical possibilities, will wish at some point in a composition to enhance some chords or groups of overtones to intensities impossible to any ordinary musical instrument or to any number of players which his stage will accommodate. For example, if he wishes to have at some moment the acoustic power of twenty piccolo players instead of one, all he needs to do is to put a high-quality loudspeaker in the player's place in the orchestra and, well shielded behind it, a microphone into which the player can perform: vacuum-tube amplification will do the rest.

If the tones he wishes are not those of an ordinary instrument a few vacuum-tube oscillators [1] can be arranged to supply the loudspeaker and the intensities of its output controlled by dials or switches. Their tones can be introduced sharply or gradually as required;

[1] An electrical source of a single musical tone of conveniently variable pitch is the widely known Theremin. This is, in effect, a howling radio set which varies its tone at the wave of its master's hand.

Two high-frequency oscillators supply their currents to a detector which produces an alternating current of a frequency equal to the difference between the frequencies of the oscillators. This current supplies the loudspeaker. This is exactly the operation described on page 51 for the heterodyne detection of continuous waves except that the two oscillators are close together instead of miles apart. In that method of radio detection the local oscillator is controlled in frequency by varying the capacity of the condenser in its tuned circuit. Mr. L. S. Theremin does the same thing but in a spectacular manner. The moving hand of the manipulator instead of turning a dial to change the capacity and hence the pitch of the beat note acts as an added plate to the tuning condenser. The capacity changes, therefore, with the position of the hand.

and a vibrato of any desired number of cycles per second be secured.

Both these methods are practical. A third method to accomplish the same thing, equally practicable, would involve recording phonographically on vertical-cut records the output of oscillators which can be adjusted in a laboratory until they combine to supply the particular tones which composer or director needs for an effect. This record would then supply the current to the loudspeaker. If several different effects are desired they may be recorded by special processes on separate strips of film. Very little mechanical ingenuity would be needed to start reproducing from the proper film record upon the depression of a key.

The last method would be anathema to many music lovers but what would have been their attitude if they had been living when inventors provided the keyboard control for a power-driven pipe organ or the mechanical hammer of the piano? Those devices developed slowly through so many centuries that they never startled anyone. The electrical devices which are today in prospect can produce complexes of musical tones far beyond the dreams of composers; they offer untold possibilities but require new skills for their use.

The schemes just described may not be dismissed with superior assurance on the mere ground that they are phonographic and incapable of reproducing music in its full quality. What the ear can recognize has been rather carefully determined; and sounds can be produced from loudspeakers which are indistinguishable from auditorium or chamber music. Phonographic recording is not necessary; there is an alternative method which avoids any loss in either pick-up or recording and assures the loudspeaker the proper current to produce any desired complex sound. The method employs some of the principles involved in the variable-area film records which were mentioned on page 140.

On such a record a pure tone appears as a space pattern; one side of the strip is black and the other transparent, with the boundary between the two parts a wavy line. This line is a plot of a sinusoid on a scale where distance along the film represents time. The distance between successive crests depends upon the frequency of the sinusoid and upon the speed at which the film travels. If the frequency is f there must be f crests in the length of film which will move past the photoelectric cell in one second; or, otherwise stated, the crests must be so spaced that each reaches the cell $1/f$ th of a second after the preceding.

If two pure tones of different frequencies and intensities are simultaneously recorded the boundary, between black and clear on the film, is a complex curve which is the graphical addition of the curves corresponding to the separate sinusoids. In this way any number of sinusoids can be combined to obtain the space pattern of the corresponding complex sound. The graphs on page 263 illustrate the method.

The wave form of any desired complex sound may be constructed by accurate mechanical drawing. All that is required is to lay out each sinusoid, making the height of its waves proportional to the amplitude desired for that component, and then to combine all these space patterns into a pattern for the synthetic sound.

This graphically constructed wave may then be photographed on a strip of film to produce a variable-area sound track. From this the synthetic sound can be obtained in the usual manner for such records.

It is not necessary to transfer the wave form to a film. Instead of the wave pattern being the boundary between opaque and clear portions of a film it may be made the edge of a strip of metal or celluloid. It forms a scalloped boundary between opacity and complete transparency. When this strip is moved along between a lamp and a photoelectric cell there is none of the background noise, which arises in the case of a film, because of its grain structure and the lack of uniform transparency in the clear portions of its sound track.

Templates of this type can be constructed to represent faithfully the complete overtone structure of any musical instrument, or for that matter of any orchestral combination of instruments. Sounds can be produced which would represent orchestral assemblies larger than any stage would usually accommodate. The wave pattern which recreates the tone of a violin can be based on the best toned instrument and the playing of a virtuoso. By this electromechanical method, there can be produced the orchestral music of an ideal and all-star organization, and the music of the different choirs can be given intensities corresponding to any desired number of players.

The mechanics of the assembly of such wave patterns and of the sequential reproduction of the corresponding sounds is not too difficult a task for electrical designers. The complexity of the control mechanisms is not even comparable to that of the equipment which goes into a dial-telephone central-office. One of the operations performed in some offices of that type is pertinent to the present discussion. It occurs in making a telephone connection from the toll office in a dial-telephone area of a large city to some manually-operated switchboard in a suburban town. The dialing of the number connects the line to the girl operator in the suburban office, who sits ready to complete the connection when told the local number of the party. She cannot interpret the dialing; and so it is arranged that it shall connect to her headphone the current from a piece of equipment known as a "call announcer". This will reproduce from film records the various digits and letters used to designate telephone lines. As each number or letter is dialed reproduction takes place from the proper record. The operator therefore hears spoken numerals and letters exactly as if from the lips of a girl at some other manual switchboard. Automatic equipment thus produces in a desired sequence complex sounds of significance.

With the details, of the necessary mechanism for picking up music-bearing currents in proper order, the musician or music lover need not be concerned. Patent literature [1] and technical magazines indicate that there

[1] Most of the manifestations of these inventions which have so far sought public recognition have taken the form of "electric organs". In general these appear to be substitutes for the bulkier pipe organs. They derive their tones either from vacuum-tube oscillators or from various designs of electromagnetic generators of alternating currents, which operate upon the same general set of principles as the power generators that supply our electric clocks and the hum in our radio sets. Another manifestation is the electric piano. In one form this is a standard piano the vibrations of the strings of which are picked up electrically for transmission instead of electro-acoustically as by a microphone. But this is not electrical music in the narrow meaning of this chapter.

are plenty of inventors at work so that adequate facilities may be anticipated. For producing the currents various methods are available of which those already described are sufficiently typical. The suggested use of individual oscillators for each component sinusoid in a complex sound would demand a very large number of oscillators. By the use, however, of templates cut to desired wave patterns the amount of apparatus is greatly reduced. Some such general method, therefore, appears to offer the most economical procedure. Libraries of templates could be constructed covering all desired combinations of tones.

Not only do the available techniques permit the combination of familiar tones but they offer to the creative musician possibilities of tones as yet unheard. Since the quality of a complex tone depends upon the relative intensities of the various harmonics of its fundamental, new qualities may be obtained by enhancing some of the overtones beyond the intensities which they can attain in the course of the natural vibrations of their sources. It is possible to go much farther and to create the most unheard-of combinations. What new sounds will prove pleasing or useful in musical compositions can be determined only by trial. A broad field of research, therefore, is opening in music.

Investigations in this field will yield also valuable information as to musical preference in matters like vibrato, portamento and attack. Vibrato, for example, is a subject of much interest, of relatively incomplete description in physical terms, and of considerable controversy among singing teachers. It appears in its simplest form in the technique of the instrumentalist, the cellist, for example, but is mechanically impossible in piano music because an intermediate lever transmits the deforming blow and the performer cannot vary the tune of the string. Vibrato seems to be an instance of what a communication engineer might call "frequency modulation". The fundamental frequency wobbles more or less periodically a few times a second. As it does so all the overtones shift correspondingly in frequency. The effect may, of course, be complicated by accompanying small changes in the modes of vibration, and in their damping. Such variations can be produced mechanically and under controlled conditions. If musical experts compared the various results a statistical determination of the most pleasing vibrato would be possible.

Most of the different variations, which inevitably occur in the production of music, are today of undetermined importance.[1] There have been almost no exact researches on the basis of which correlations might be established between these variations and pleasurable sensations or emotion. A mere listing of the most important factors indicates the magnitude of our present ignorance.

In the first place as to a listener: His auditory threshold varies from day to day by several decibels. It is not the same, except on a statistical basis, as that of his neighbor in the next seat in the orchestra. The interference pattern in the hall shifts and varies, with the

[1] Some authorities believe that true artistry must possess the contradictory aspects of uniformity and individuality. In certain aspects all artists conform, in other aspects they differ, and the differences are as important as the conformances in producing a really great artist.

result that he gets at any instant a markedly different sound from his neighbor. An illustration of the magnitude of this effect is plotted on page 258. There is no stability to the pattern; it is different for each frequency in the entire range of audible tones. Even for the same tones it is different if they arise from different points on the stage since that will mean different paths, different reflections and absorption, and different amounts of interference or reenforcement at each position throughout the auditorium.

The auditorium conditions change, slowly rather than suddenly, due to changes in temperature which affect transmission of sound through air, in humidity, and in the size and arrangement of the audience. These may make an encore an acoustical product very different physically from that of an earlier rendition. They will make one performance unlike another although the variations are probably not greater in effect than those which occur in the hearing ability and attention of the average listener.

Finally, as to the musicians: There are physical limits closer than which they cannot perceive differences in pitch; hence there are differences in the tune of the various instruments even of the same kind. Between the musicians there are inevitably differences of tempo. Only within certain limits can they all draw their bows at the same instant. There are differences in their attack, their style of play, their vibrato or what not. The music of a single violin picked up and proportionately amplified is not the music of ten violins playing in unison.

That statement of fact brings out the important question as to synthetic music. Is perfection desired or an average of imperfection? If the world's best performer on each orchestral instrument could be cast in a divine mold so that there would be sufficient of his equals to man an orchestra, would that make for better music? If the instruments which were played by all those from the same mold were identical and tuned to a precision such as is obtainable for alternating currents and were played by their star performers in time, with equal precision, would an audience enjoy it, or would there be the feeling that the music was mechanical and monotonous?

To illustrate what is meant by precision: There are oscillators [1] in Bell Laboratories that have run for years at frequencies which keep time to an accuracy of one one-hundred thousandth part of a second. Their frequencies can be compared to the astounding accuracy of one part in ten billion. If two identical motor cars with engines running at the same speed to that accuracy entered upon a race they would have to travel more than 2000 miles before one car would be ahead of the other by a distance equal to the thickness of the enamel on its bumper.

Techniques and mechanisms are available which will permit the production of musical tones with a precision beyond that required by the ear of a listener and beyond that possible to human performers. The latter are subject not only to the limitations and variations of performance which have just been listed but also to all those temperamental and psychological variations in ability which accompany human effort, particularly in

[1] Cf. Chapter 11, "Signals and Speech".

the artistic activities and in golf. More consistent and more perfect, or ideal, performance can be obtained from electromechanical equipment. It "can be" in the sense that it is physically possible but its commercial accomplishment waits for an effective economic urge and a great deal of engineering and manufacturing development. It will not arrive overnight, but gradually. But it is inevitable that sooner or later, on a scale small or grand, there will be a real production of synthetic music in all its possible perfection. "Customer acceptance" will remain to be determined. And thus will arise the previous question as to whether perfection is desirable.

Adopt for the moment what may be the short-sighted view that it will not be desirable, that human imperfections will be preferred, and that human emotions must enter into the production of music as well as into its composition. Two lines of further progress can then be anticipated. One will be toward the quantitative study of the amount, character, and frequency of occurrence of musical imperfections which are preferred by music lovers and music patrons. When that has been determined the wave forms of the synthetic music can be drawn to include such imperfections. There will still remain the possibility of the human control of the equipment by the musical director. Instead of waving a baton in an effort to express his ideas and emotions through a hundred human musicians he may turn dials and push keys, performing upon an essentially perfect source of musical tones.

George Bernard Shaw made once—perhaps it was more than once—a careless wisecrack. The epigram that "Those who can, do; and those who can't, teach" is so fast that it slips past the border of the mind without visé of logic. Teacher and artist work in different media and are no more directly comparable than painter and singer, or poet and engineer. The medium in which the teacher works, and through which his inspiration must be effective, is the mind of his pupil.

His task demands more than the ability to inspire. He must know both medium and technique; he must be ingenious but accurate in analysis and creative in synthesis.

It is in analysis that he will wish to employ such apparatus for scientific measurements as may be available. Fads in equipment he will avoid, and quackery, unconscious as well as conscious. He will prefer a little machinery, which he understands thoroughly, that will give clear and definite data of a useful character. In its selection engineering principles will be applied since the equipment he needs should be adapted to accomplish a necessary pedagogical purpose in an accurate convenient manner and at an economical price.

Some electro-acoustical apparatus which might be of service to teachers of music is at present available or in prospect. Its description in this chapter is not to be read as a prescription, for that would be in the nature of presumption, certainly on the part of the writer. It would probably be so even on the part of the physicists and engineers whose researches are reported in this book. The physicist, per se, can pick-up and analyze the product of the musician; he can measure its physical magnitudes and correlate them with what the human ear can perceive; but esthetic judgment as to the product is the province of the musician and particularly of the critically trained teacher. On the other hand both musician and teacher might gain in effectiveness by adopting some of the exactness of statement and terminology of the scientist and by avoiding unconscious bunk.

As an illustration there is a widely spread idea that the finger of a pianist can affect the sound of a note by its motion after it has struck the key. All the range of tone which any pianist can get from a given piano *through his fingers* can be produced by a simple apparatus. Mount a tube vertically above a piano key. Suspend in the tube by a string a lead sinker, like that of a fisherman, which is padded to protect the ivory. Let this weight drop through the tube from various heights and it will produce all the tone that can be produced by any finger technique. Nevertheless some teachers claim a difference and want equipment which will show their pupils just the difference in tone due to what a billiardist might call "body English". "The moving finger writes and having writ moves on" and so also does the finger of the pianist. The momentum of his blow—sometimes hers, judging from those who have advanced the idea to the writer—has been transferred to the hammer of the piano; and the subsequent events

are as completely out of hand as a skidding automobile
to a back-seat driver. "A little science now and then
is relished by the best of men; and would not misbecome
a musician".

Schools of music, and particularly those which have
funds and time to devote to research in music and in
its related psychology, will find already designed about
all the equipment that would be needed. Most of the
devices, however, are beyond either the needs or the
financial resources of most individual teachers.

One device to which all musicians should have access
is the audiometer by which there can be determined
thresholds of hearing. Teachers especially should know
if their hearing is normal and if not to what extent
and in what range of frequencies. Periodic, perhaps
annual, tests of hearing would not appear out of place
for those who judge by ear. As an illustration from
another field: it is sometimes good business for a man
whose heart action has been questioned by an examiner
for a life insurance company to appeal for re-examina-
tion by one of the older heart specialists. There is the
chance that the hearing of the older ear may not be so
acute for the higher frequency and fainter murmurs.

As one grows older his upper limit of audible frequencies drops rapidly; even in the thirties it is likely
to be down several thousand cycles from the extreme
20-22,000 which youth can detect. This extreme upper
range, of course, is not of great importance; but any
deficiency below the 12-15,000 cycles, which are essential to the complete naturalness of most musical notes
and of ordinary sounds, might well be known and
allowed for in the judgment of sounds.

Audiometers are probably in the price range for many schools but when their use would not be economical otologists could be consulted; in universities sometimes the psychology department or the office of the university doctor is equipped for such tests. In public school systems facilities are usually lacking for measuring the thresholds at various pitches throughout the audible range. Such institutions are more likely to have the so-called 4-A audiometer which permits a rapid overall test of hearing for the band of frequencies involved in speech and discloses abnormalities which should be investigated.

For a school of considerable size one or two soundproof rooms of adjustable reverberation time might be of value. The simplest construction involves a series of panels reaching from floor to ceiling and hinged like doors. The opposite sides of each panel are differently treated acoustically, one, for example, a smooth firm reflecting surface and the other of felt so as to be highly absorptive. The panels fit against the sides of the room like blind doors. When one is swung through 180 degrees it exposes the portion of the wall it has previously covered and covers an equal area with the acoustic material of its reverse side. By varying the exposed sides of the paneling the reverberation time can be adjusted through a wide range of values. By exposing highly absorbing surfaces part of the way around a room and reflecting surfaces for the rest a "live-dead-end" studio may be formed of a type of present interest in radio.

When the research program justifies the expenditure, a high-quality system can be installed; a microphone in the studio, amplifiers in an intermediate room, and a loudspeaker in another studio. Electrical measurements of what the microphone picks up and control of what the loudspeaker delivers can be carried out in the intermediate room; and audience reactions judged in the second studio. The nature of the researches will determine the additional electrical equipment.

A piece of apparatus which frequently interests teachers of music is a projection oscilloscope. This device can be pictured conveniently by imagining a very small mirror to be fastened to the diaphragm of a loud speaker. As the diaphragm bends the mirror tilts. Upon the mirror falls a narrow beam of light from a nearby lamp. After reflection this beam falls upon a much larger mirror which is one face of a rotating mirror. The latter might be formed by eight rectangular mirrors which stand on edge on a turntable and are grouped, reflecting surfaces outward, to form an octagon. The face, of this system of mirrors, catches the beam from the tilting mirror and reflects it to a screen where it appears as a spot of light. When the loudspeaker element operates the mirror vibrates and the spot dances up and down, but too fast to be seen except as a bright vertical streak. If, while no current flows and the vibrating mirror is still, the rotating mirror is turned, the spot of light is drawn across the screen. Just as it passes beyond the screen the next mirror of the octagon comes into position to pick up the beam. It is reflected to the opposite side of the screen, and then swept across. If the table turns fast enough the successive travels across the screen can not be distinguished; and what appears is a continuous horizontal line.

When the rotating mirror and the vibrating mirror are both in operation the up-and-down motion due to the latter is spread out and the spot traces a wavy line on the screen—a space pattern of the current which actuates the vibrating mirror. The greater the current, the larger the amplitude of the waves; the higher the speed of the revolving mirror, the longer the wavelength of the pattern on the screen. This means more detail to the picture and more opportunity of distinguishing the finer wiggles due to the harmonics in the wave, particularly if the spot of light is small so that the trace is a fine line. There is a limit, however, to the detail because resolution, as it is called, is accomplished at the expense of brightness and consequently of visibility.

The analogy is with exposure time in snapshot photography, with the eye acting as the camera. Fast-moving objects must be correspondingly bright to be seen. The result is that projection oscilloscopes can not present the details of complex wave forms with anything like completeness. They show usually only the fundamental and the most prominent lower-frequency harmonics. About the most that can be expected from such devices was demonstrated by oscilloscopes at the Chicago Exposition of 1933 in the exhibits of the General Motors Company and of the Bell System, and by an improved instrument of the Bell System at San Diego in 1935.

The projection oscilloscope is a fascinating instrument to watch and to play with; but it is doubtful if playing to it would develop much worthwhile data. It shows best sustained tones. Rapid variations such as occur in portamento or in the slide from one tone to another, in "attack" and in other problems of technique are almost impossible to observe; and frequency variations like those of vibrato are not distinguishable by eye.

Wave analysis can be made by oscillographic methods but it requires an instrument which forms a very fine trace directly upon a sensitized film. After being photographically recorded the wave form is enlarged to a size much larger than the waves on the screen of a projection oscilloscope. Then it is analyzed by mathematical methods. When an accurate analysis is desired the wave must be recorded by a high-quality and high-speed oscillograph. Suitable instruments cost thousands of dollars to construct and usually require expert operation by technicians. There are fifteen or twenty such instruments in constant use in the Bell Laboratories, but most of them for the study of current variations which have no speech or musical significance. When the recorded wave is that of a complex sound its analysis used to take days but now through an ingenious graphical method an analysis disclosing twenty or thirty of the harmonics can be made in three hours. Thousands of dollars of equipment and hours of expert time are required to find out about a complex wave. It would appear, therefore, that oscillographic methods are more for research than for teaching.

Instead of a projection oscilloscope which forms a pretty but evanescent pattern, or instead of the high-speed oscillograph which is primarily a research instrument, there might be more usefulness to schools and individual teachers in some type of reed analyzer. This instrument, like an oscillograph, requires auxiliary apparatus of high-quality microphone and amplifier. The current output from the amplifier is delivered simultaneously to a large number of receiver elements. In each of these there is a reed which is set into forced vibration by the current. Each reed is tuned to a definite frequency and responds with the greatest amplitude of motion to a current component of the same frequency. To frequencies separated from the resonant frequency by an interval of a quarter of a semitone the response of the reed is negligible. For smaller intervals the amount of motion, for the same intensity of current, increases disproportionately as the interval decreases. In one model of this type of analyzer there are 144 reeds covering at equal intervals the frequency range from 50 to 3200 cycles per second.

The reeds are mounted side by side and viewed end-on so that in quiescence they appear like a row of dots. When a complex current, involving frequencies within the range of the device, is supplied to it the pattern changes. Some of the reeds are forced to vibrate and these no longer appear as dots but as fuzzy vertical lines with lengths proportional to their amplitudes of vibration. By noting what reeds are affected, and estimating to what extent, a fairly accurate picture is obtained of the components in a complex current. For a single note the analyzer gives at a glance the overtone structure. A camera can be used to photograph the pattern of the reeds and so to furnish a record for further study.

This reed analyzer permits a comparison of the overtone structure of similar notes produced under different conditions or by different performers, as for example similar notes of different singers. Although it has such possibilities it is probably more of a research tool than a teaching aid. Suppose it does tell a teacher how the sung vowel "ah" differs in overtone structure from another vowel sound, or the difference between the note of a pupil and that of a singer who has arrived. The facts it gives are physical, and mathematical in their expression. Unless, or until, facts of that character have been correlated by research with the physiology of throat, larynx and mouth they are lifeless and, however interesting, of small value to teachers. Even after the large amount of research which is probably the preliminary has been carried out, there will still remain the very difficult pedagogical problem of translating its results into instructions which a student can comprehend and apply.

Oscilloscope and frequency analyzer may be what teachers need, despite the preceding description of their functions. One presents a wave form and the other a "frequency spectrum". Both can present records of a student's performance which can serve as a basis for discussion by the teacher. The only difficulty is to know what conclusions can be drawn from such records which would be an aid in teaching.

The pupil is a musician; with all that implies. He is not a mathematical physicist and it may be of little assistance to him to know that his upper resonance in certain vowel tones is down 20 db from the accepted ideal. If he could sit beside his teacher and hear himself as others hear him, his own musical ear, guided by immediate criticism, would find out what was wrong in his performance. Knowing how he sounded and knowing from his observations of other musicians how he would like to sound, he would be in a position to appreciate what he had to learn and to discuss with the teacher the necessary corrections of his imperfect technique.

To hear oneself as others hear him would seem to be the basis for self criticism and consequent improvement. To have a mirror for one's voice might, for coloring, be as helpful as is the mirror in a vanity case for the face. But the mirror must reflect truthfully and without distortion. Such high-quality equipment as is used today for motion pictures would be excellently fitted except for its cost, its bulk and the necessity of operation by technicians. As a rule only artists who are paid as popular favorites can afford the luxury of self criticism from high-quality records.

All musicians, like all public speakers and actors, hear themselves as they perform but never can they do so as do those in the audience. They may know how their production must sound to them if it is to stimulate the audience reaction which they desire; but it is physically impossible for a vocalist to hear himself as others hear him. Probably the nearest approach to objectivity in listening to oneself occurs in the case of an organist while he plays by itself an echo organ in the rear of the hall. Because of the acoustic conditions, if for no other reason, an orchestra director can never hear exactly the music which his audience receives.

That a performer is most keenly aware of his own performance goes without proof. Who was it who first said: If I didn't practise I would know the difference in my performance immediately; next the critics would notice it; and finally the public. It is not a question of intentness or of critical ability: it is a question of the location of the viewing point. A painter may know what every brush mark, and added layer of pigment, will accomplish but nevertheless, at some time or other, he steps back from the easel to the viewing point of his critics and his public. The actor makes up before his mirror. He may know how each inflection of his voice must sound to him if it is to get over the desired effect; but there is no mirror for his voice unless he is recorded. And if that is well done he can then hear himself as others hear him.

Magnetic recording promises to be the economical solution of the problem. The frequency range it covers today extends to about 5500 cycles; which compares favorably with the range the radio has familiarized. It will handle about the same intensity range; and its background noise is about the same as a lateral-cut phonograph record. The entire apparatus, consisting of magnetic recorder, amplifiers and loudspeaker, can be assembled into a cabinet about the size of a console radio set or into a couple of cases about as large as a suitcase.

Current from the microphone, after amplification, passes to two small electromagnets the cores of which end in polepieces shaped like a chisel. As the current varies, the magnetism of these cores varies correspondingly. Their sharp edges face each other across a narrow gap through which passes a thin steel tape. As the current varies, this tape is subjected to a proportional magnetization. Thus a record of the current is stored in the tape in the form of a magnetic pattern.

To reproduce from the tape it is passed through a similar gap between another pair of polepieces. The total of magnetism, in the magnetic circuit of cores, polepieces and gap, varies therefore with what the moving tape contributes. Hence the current in the coils around the cores also varies. These variations in current, when amplified and supplied to a loudspeaker, reproduce the original sound.

The tape runs between two reels, like the ribbon of a typewriter, and passes en route through both the recording and the reproducing magnets. A record can be made for a length of time corresponding to the available length of tape; three to fifteen minutes worth of tape doesn't require very large drums for its storage. After a record is made the tape is rewound and started through again. On that trip, however, the microphone is cut off, and the loudspeaker is connected through the amplifier to the coils of the reproducing magnet. The entire record can be repeated as many times as is desired; and since the rewind can be accomplished at much higher speed a very short time can separate the repetitions. If one wishes to concentrate attention upon a single phrase it is only necessary to reproduce from the tape until that phrase is reached and then repeat it as frequently as desired. When a new record is to be produced, use is made of another pair of magnets through which the tape passes just before it reaches the recording element. These demagnetize the tape, wiping out its magnetic pattern. They are normally inoperative but can be thrown into action by the proper switch.

Permanent records by this method could only be obtained for preservation by taking off the tape or by a process of dubbing or rerecording from the tape onto film or disc. The device, therefore, is not in competition with film or disc which have the advantage of ease in the duplication of records. It is of primary value in recording for immediate reproduction.

In that regard it would appear to be ideal for any teacher of instrumental or vocal expression who would like to show a pupil just how he sounded immediately after he had made the sound. Two of these devices have been placed in the hands of the public to let it know how its voice sounds when it telephones. One was operated as a Bell System Exhibit at San Diego during 1935 and the other is a loan exhibit of the Bell Telephone Company of Pennsylvania to the Franklin Institute in Philadelphia. Those particular exhibits are arranged to record for five seconds and then to reproduce during the next five. Reproduction is through telephone receivers. Through those receivers may listen the friends of the person who wishes to hear his own telephone voice. He talks into an ordinary handset telephone. As he does so they hear him through their receivers. During the next five seconds the magnetic recorder reproduces what he said in all the receivers, including that of the handset. In that way the observers hear the spoken words, first transmitted directly and then reproduced. When the speaker expresses surprise and doubt, as is typical, and says: "Do I really talk like that?" they are able to say: "But that is exactly the way you sounded the first time". If music teachers can get any teaching assistance from being put in a similar position with reference to their pupils the necessary apparatus has been developed.

17

In the Marine Biological Laboratory at Plymouth (England) it was proved that the common eel was sensitive to a frequency, transmitted through the water, of about 340 cycles per second. All you have to do to test the hearing of a fish is to submerge a buzzer, or a telephone receiver, excite it at the proper frequency and at the same time feed the fish. It acquires a conditioned reflex—compare the work of the famous Russian, Pavlov, on dinner signals for dogs. After a while one fails to serve the meal but counts the guests the signal has attracted. Some fish are reported bright enough to get the idea in three trials; and it is usually assumed that one which can't learn after a hundred dinner invitations is not stupid but congenitally deaf.

Grasshoppers have their ears just below the knee joints of the forelegs; and are credited with responding to a range of frequency from about 500 to 28,000 cycles. When one male starts singing his rivals take up the contest. Not much is known about their ears; but that they hear each other was proved by the experiment of destroying the eardrums of a large number of grasshoppers who thereafter showed no vocal rivalry.

Birds have only about a sixth as many transverse fibers in their basilar membranes as do humans; and do not have nearly the ability to discriminate between tones which one would expect from their vocal powers.

Dogs, on the other hand, can discriminate between notes a quarter of a semitone apart. Some experiments point to a sense of "absolute pitch" on their part. They seem able also to differentiate between notes on the basis of their intensities. Many of the stories as to their acuity of hearing—instances where they hear in advance of their masters—probably mean merely that their attention is more concentrated on possible sounds. Their thresholds of audibility can not be appreciably below that of humans because for the human ear the threshold is only about eleven decibels above the limiting noise level of thermal agitation.

*   *   *   *   *

The cochlea and basilar membrane of the human ear, unlike other organs of the body, are the same size a month or two after birth as at maturity. If the basilar membrane changed in length its vibration pattern for the same complex note would be different and one's sense of pitch would change as he grew older. A child, as it matured, would have to be conditioned over and over again to the sound of its mother's voice; and musical prodigies would have difficulty in developing. In hearing there is no counterpart to change of voice.

*   *   *   *   *

A serviceable concept of what 50 decibels represent may be obtained from a simple experiment upon one's own person. While in the presence of a loud sound close both ear canals using a finger to depress the tragus of each ear until it covers the entrance to the canal. If the sound is loud it can still be heard but much fainter. Its power at the ear drum is reduced to about one one-hundred thousandth part of its original value. This is

a crude experiment, of course, liable to individual variations but 50 db is the average reduction which that
procedure produced for a few scientists in the Bell Laboratories who years ago tried this test upon themselves.
How could they tell it was 50 db? By listening alternately to two similar sounds under the two conditions
of tragus depressed and not depressed while varying the
relative intensity of the sounds until they were perceived as equally loud under the two conditions. From
the values of the alternating currents which produced
the sounds the difference in level was immediately
obtainable.

*   *   *   *   *

When a pure tone of steady pitch is varied cyclically
in intensity the result is not a pure tone. What takes
place is modulation, the fundamental operation of electrical communication. If the note has a frequency of f
and the intensity changes n times a second the result
is three pure tones, one of frequency f, that of the
original, and the others $f + n$ and $f - n$. Varying a
note of 300 cycles five times a second produces notes of
295, 300, and 305 cycles. If the variation is complete,
from full intensity to zero, the intensities of these three
notes are in the ratio of $1/4$, $1/2$, and $1/4$.

A different sort of modulation takes place if the
original note is periodically changed in pitch. To avoid
for the moment the effect of overtones deal with a pure
note such as would be produced by a vacuum-tube oscillator. Its control dial, which tunes it up or down in
frequency, is swung back and forth producing a variation through a definite musical interval. What now
takes place is much more complicated. In general there

is produced a series of tones above the original and a similar series below. Let the variation in pitch occur five times a second. Then there will be tones of 305, 310, 315, and so on; and of 295, 290, 285, as well as one of 300 cycles. The relative intensities of the component tones will depend upon the musical interval through which the frequency is varied.

This is what takes place in vibrato. Contrary to the instinctive impression a note played, or sung, with vibrato is not of constant pitch and varying intensity. Instead it is a whole family of tones of different pitches and constant intensities. The proof is either mathematical analysis of the sound, or experimental, for example, with the reed analyzer described on page 206. The vibrato in singing discloses a swing as large as a semitone.

According to some observers the variations in a good vibrato occur six to seven times a second. The tremolo, its inartistic extreme, is the result of uncoordinated muscular tension; and its variation, which is uneven, is often faster than in the vibrato.

* * * * *

An extreme illustration of irregularity in an auditorium was given by P. E. Sabine in his text on "Acoustics and Architecture". He described for a well known concert hall certain effects which occur on the stage but are not apparent to the audience. Due to reflections, primarily from the curved walls of the stage, the conductor finds it hard to secure for his position a satisfactory balance of the instruments. The organist in his position can hardly hear certain instruments at all. To the violinist in the front row the wood winds seem to be "rolling down on his head from the ceiling". To one on the stage a piano solo seems to be accompanied by a whole row of performers located in the rear of the hall. Of importance when concerts are broadcast is the fact that the microphone picks up audience noises, like coughing, and a greater amount of reverberant sound than is experienced in the body of the hall. The condition is unusual but it merely goes to show what wide differences may physically exist in music that is supposedly the same for all listeners.

Reverberation time is measured for a note of 512 cycles per second. For other frequencies the time required for a pure tone to decay by 60 db will be appreciably different.

The reverberation in a hall will vary with the humidity of its atmosphere. In dry air the high frequencies are strongly absorbed. That means that when the humidity is high the high frequencies suffer less in their travels between reflections and so the sound decays less rapidly. A curve showing the relation appears on page 260.

*　　*　　*　　*　　*

The absorption of sound by walls and their coverings is different for tones of different frequencies. A felt, each square foot of which is equivalent to 0.13 square foot of open window for a tone of 128 cycles, is equivalent to 0.41 square foot at 256 cycles; to 0.56 at 512; 0.69 at 1024; 0.65 at 2048; and 0.49 at 4096. There is no general rule for the relation between absorption and frequency. Some draperies, for example, have an absorption of 0.06 at 128, and 0.08, 0.13, 0.23, 0.40 and 0.44 at the successive octaves up to 4096 cycles. Even orchestra chairs absorb different frequencies in different amounts. The net result of the reflections and absorptions in any hall is that the different tones of music undergo markedly different acoustic treatments. Since the reverberant sound in a hall is four to ten times as great as the direct, differences in reverberation and in standing-wave pattern determine largely what a listener hears; and all don't receive anywhere near the same music.

* * * * *

A teaching method employing head receivers has been described by Captain R. H. Ranger for the training of a choir of singers. A phonograph record is made of each vocal part as rendered by one of the best available voices and embodying the preferred interpretation. Those who sing that part practise under the leadership of the recorded voice as delivered to them through individual head receivers. Instruction en masse is thus possible, remarkably fast progress and, generally, results as excellent as the individual voices permit. The voice in the telephone receivers is their guide and they are not distracted by one another's errors. Each singer is, in effect, singing duo with an instructor.

Bass, baritone, contralto and soprano parts may be led individually but all synchronized without serious technical difficulty. It is a very efficient method of training a large choir, particularly useful when many of its singers are relatively inexperienced.

The only difficulty is the economic one. Equipment for recording, if it is to cover a wide range of frequencies free from distortion, is expensive in first cost and in operation. Perhaps the magnetic method of recording will supply the future need. Under this method no permanent record is made; as soon as one part is learned another could be recorded. But how it will develop is not known at this writing since only experimental models have been constructed. Technically, however, suitable recording is assured by one method or another; and musicians who look far enough into the future can assume its availability.

*   *   *   *   *

How persistent certain popular misconceptions may be is illustrated by the idea of a pianist's control which was discussed on page 200. "But", say those who dissent from that statement, "we have heard Paderewski play just one note, and we know it could not have been produced by a purely mechanical blow—an impulse due to a weight dropping on the key with proper velocity". It may be idle to say that the listener is conditioned for that single note by all that has gone before, from the general anticipation, which led to the decision to attend that recital, to the specific, occasioned by all the artistry of composer and pianist, up to the pause which preceded that particular note. It is sometimes even futile to explain that a few years ago various scientists interested in the manufacture of pianos investigated the question by taking oscillographic records of the sounds produced by different finger techniques. The oscillograms disclosed no differences in the musical character of the sound.

The story is told that a woman to whom these physical facts were explained remarked that she had always felt that this should be so, that it wasn't the touch of the artist that made the difference but his soul.

Sometimes research moves to its conclusions very rapidly. Until it has done so prophecy is dangerous. It now appears possible, however, that a scale of loudness may be found which will have steps more satisfying than those discussed in Chapter 7. Perhaps after all one does judge the loudness of complex musical sounds, of speech, and of noise, in increments more or less analogous to the minimum perceptible increments for pure tones. If that proves to be so there may turn out to be some unit of loudness which meets the psychological and physiological requirements. The range from zero loudness, that is inaudibility, to the maximum which excites pain will then involve two or three hundred of these units. Twice as loud will mean twice the number of loudness units. On the other hand it may not turn out that way at all. For the present one cannot go farther than the facts stated in Chapter 7.

* * * * *

When one takes into account the directional pattern of the direct sound from musical instruments, the various patterns of the reverberant sound which are so different at different positions even closely nearby in an auditorium, and the different absorption which different frequencies of vibration experience in ordinary air, one will realize that the individuals of an audience do not hear the same music. Differences sometimes as high as 30 decibels may occur between the sounds imposed upon auditors in different seats. Ten db of difference, in the intensity of the same harmonic, is probably the least that can be expected for high-frequency tones in a large auditorium.

Even if two musical critics at a performance have

identical audiograms—and that is most improbable—they cannot hear exactly the same music because they cannot both be in the same place at once.

There is only one way that critics can be assured of listening to the same music. If it is picked up by a high-quality microphone and supplied to carefully matched pairs of head receivers, then both can get the same sound. It would not assist at all in securing equality in what they listen to, if the music was delivered by a loud-speaker; for then all the causes of variation would be effective which were mentioned above.

No one knows how much differences in judgment are effected by such differences in what the listeners receive. In judging a work of graphic art it can be assured that what is exposed to the eye of one critic is exposed to that of any other. Temperamental differences and differences of visual acuity, of course, still exist but at least the critics can talk about the same thing. In music they cannot—not within several decibels throughout most of the frequency range.

* * * * *

The frequency range of radio is what it is as a result of a number of factors, no one of which is a physical limitation. Nominally it transmits a range from 100 to 5000 cycles. The assignment of wave lengths to broadcasting stations is on the basis of a separation of 10,000 cycles between nearby stations. Thus one station might have, as assigned frequency of its carrier, 700,000 cycles and another station, 710,000. The 700,000-cycle station in transmitting a pure tone of 4500 cycles would send out "ether" waves of frequency 700,000 less 4500 or 695,500 and 700,000 plus 4500 or 704,500, in addition to its carrier wave of 700,000 cycles. The other station in the situation transmits 705,500, 710,000 and 714,500. If the audio frequency is 5000 cycles then one station sends out 705,000 cycles for its upper sideband which is just the same as, and so interfering with, the 705,000-cycle lower sideband of the other station. By the assignment of wavelengths, therefore, radio stations are restricted to a 5000-cycle band of audio frequencies.

Some of the more powerful stations in transmitting from their own studios—not from some distant pick-up—will send out all tones in their programs up to 7500 or more cycles a second. In the immediate neighborhood of such a station, under such a condition, radio listeners with suitable receiving sets get at least an extra half octave of the actual sounds the performers produce in the studio. Except in that very unusual condition radio listeners cannot get more than 5000 cycles. The stations do not send it out; and where their programs come from distant points they travel on program circuits which transmit only that range.

Home receiving sets are the product of the two usual commercial factors, namely, what the public will buy and what the manufacturer makes to sell. Experience apparently has shown that the majority of radio fans don't care for, and/or cannot afford sets capable of receiving much more than the range 100 to 3000 cycles, with a volume range, between the noise level of hum and the peaks of sound, perhaps 30 db but not much more. They object to the shrillness of higher frequencies even though these exist in the actual music and they prefer the more "mellow" tones.

That is a serious matter. Thousands of persons are

getting accustomed to music which lacks all natural-ness or brilliancy. They neither demand nor care for a faithful reproduction. If they constitute the paying ma-jority whose mass purchases of the radio sets of mass production keep that industry going and supply its profits; and if they constitute the mass consumers of the products advertised on the radio, it is obvious that there will be small effective demand for increasing the present range of either volume or frequency. The net result can only be that those who might wish to hear music transmitted by radio and reproduced with a range of volume and frequency satisfactory to their tastes, will not be able to do so. The serious matter is that electrical means of transmitting and reproducing music may tend to a standardization of such reproduc-tion at an esthetically low level.

Better radio sets run from about 50 to 4500 cycles with a range from noise to distorting overload of about 40 db. That will reproduce very well about all that radio normally transmits. The best sets, for which the demand is very small indeed, insufficient as a rule to encourage manufacturers to improved designs and greater produc-tion, will handle from about 40 to about 8000 cycles with a volume range about 50 db.

The limiting factors in the faithfulness with which radio can transmit music are taste, economics, and gov-ernmental requirements. Apparatus and techniques are available, whenever there is effective demand, to trans-mit by wire and by radio all of music which the ear can hear. Until that demand arises those who would like to hear more than the majority must be disappointed.

Sound-picture recording and reproduction are constantly improving in their equipment and techniques. For the ultimate future the safe assumption is that methods for recording and reproducing music will cover the entire range of frequencies and intensities which the human ear can appreciate.

Direct transmission by wire, as has been explained, has already, in the experimental case, satisfied the requirements of the ear and gone farther in the way of controlled modification of the overtone structure of music and of increase in its intensity range.

The possibilities for the electrical transmission and reproduction of music should be judged, therefore, by the best that is possible even if it is not economically practicable as of the moment, just as the possibilities of music should be judged from the performance of its masters and virtuosi and not from the renditions of amateur night.

PART FOUR

PLOTS AND GRAPHS

This book is finished except for those readers who will find of value a brief résumé in tabular form, or graphical, of the material in the preceding text. There will also be presented numerical data which will supplement the discussion of the earlier chapters. Each table or chart is accompanied by a brief explanation and sometimes by a numerical illustration of its use. Except as typographical convenience has required, the data follow the same order as the discussions of the text. Much of it is reprinted by permission from the Bell System Technical Monographs, in which case it is identified by the number of the monograph.

MUSICAL NOTES AND FREQUENCIES—Table 1, computed on the basis of 440 cycles per second for A, gives the frequencies of *the fundamentals* of musical notes within four octaves of middle C (i.e. C_3). For example, F$\sharp$ above C_3 has a fundamental component of frequency 370 cycles per second. If $F_3\sharp$ is played on a stringed instrument the frequencies of its harmonics are 370; 740; 1110; 1480; 1850; 2220; 2590; 2960; and so on; corresponding to the fundamental of $F_3\sharp$; $F_4\sharp$; $C_5\sharp$; $F_5\sharp$; approximately $A_5\sharp$; $C_6\sharp$; almost E_6; and $F_6\sharp$.

TABLE 1

	C_1-C_0	C_0-C_1	C_1-C_2	C_2-C_3	C_3-C_4	C_4-C_5	C_5-C_6	C_6-C_7
C	16.36	32.70	65.40	130.8	261.6	523.2	1046.5	2093.0
C$\sharp$	17.33	34.65	69.30	138.6	277.2	554.4	1108.7	2217.5
D	18.36	36.71	73.43	146.8	293.7	587.3	1174.7	2349.3
D$\sharp$	19.44	38.88	77.76	155.6	311.1	622.3	1244.5	2489.0
E	20.60	41.20	82.40	164.8	329.6	659.3	1318.5	2637.0
F	21.84	43.68	87.35	174.6	349.2	698.5	1396.9	2793.9
F$\sharp$	23.12	46.25	92.50	185.0	370.0	740.0	1480.0	2960.0
G	24.51	49.02	98.03	196.0	392.0	784.0	1568.0	3136.0
G$\sharp$	25.96	51.91	103.8	207.7	415.3	830.6	1661.2	3322.4
A	27.50	55.00	110.0	220.0	440.0	880.0	1760.0	3520.0
A$\sharp$	29.13	58.26	116.5	233.1	466.2	932.3	1864.7	3729.3
B	30.87	61.75	123.5	247.0	493.9	987.8	1975.5	3951.0
C	32.70	65.40	130.8	261.6	523.2	1046.5	2093.0	4186.0

DECIBEL SCALE—Table 2 gives the ratios for successive steps on the decibel scale. When, for example, two sounds are alike in acoustic power the ratio of their powers is 1.00 and the difference between them is zero decibels. If the ratio is greater than 1.00 read up in the middle column; e.g. if it is 3.16 the larger power is 5 db above the smaller. When the ratio is less than unity read down, e.g. 0.316 is 5 db below. For every 10 db shift, the decimal point moves one place; e.g. 0.0063 is —22 db; 0.063 is —12 db; 0.63 is —2 db; 6.3 is 8 db; and so on.

The values in Table 2 are in some instances convenient approximations, e.g. the ratio for 3 db is 1.996 and for 6 db 3.981 instead of 2.00 and 4.00 respectively.

Fractions of a decibel are of occasional interest. If two powers are in the ratio of 1.023 one is 0.1 db higher than the other. The ratios corresponding to 0.2 db, 0.3 db and so on to 0.9 db are respectively 1.047; 1.071; 1.098; 1.122; 1.148; 1.175; 1.202; and 1.237. For example when two powers differ by 0.4 db one is approximately 10 percent larger than the other.

TABLE 2

db	Ratio	db	Ratio	db	Ratio
—10	0.100	10	10.00	30	1000
—11	.0800	9	8.00	29	800
—12	.0630	8	6.30	29	630
—13	.0501	7	5.01	27	501
—14	.0400	6	4.00	26	400
—15	.0316	5	3.16	25	316
—16	.0251	4	2.51	24	251
—17	.0200	3	2.00	23	200
—18	.0158	2	1.58	22	158
—19	.0126	1	1.26	21	126
—20	.01000	0	1.000	20	100.
—21	.00800	—1	.800	19	80.
—22	.00630	—2	.630	18	63.
—23	.00501	—3	.501	17	50.1
—24	.00400	—4	.400	16	40.
—25	.00316	—5	.316	15	31.6
—26	.00251	—6	.251	14	25.1
—27	.00200	—7	.200	13	20.
—28	.00158	—8	.158	12	15.8
—29	.00126	—9	.126	11	12.6
—30	.00100	—10	0.100	10	10.0

THRESHOLDS OF AUDIBILITY AND OF FEELING—Figure
1 shows the range of pure tones which are audible to
the normal ear. The horizontal scale represents frequency. This scale is not "linear" but is divided into

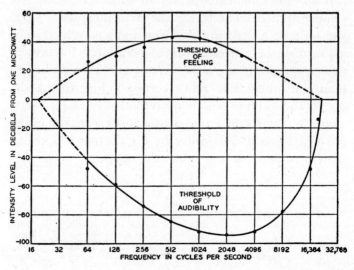

Figure 1

equal parts for each octave, starting with a keynote of
frequency 16 cycles per second. The vertical scale represents the intensity of the tone. It is divided into equal
parts for each twenty decibels, starting with a reference
intensity of one microwatt per square centimeter. For
any audible frequency there are two limiting intensities: one, that below which the ear cannot hear and
the other, that above which pain is the sensation. For
example, at frequency 512 the lowest intensity which
the ear can hear is —85 db and the highest 43. At that

frequency the ear can hear a tone the power of which is more than 1/300,000,000 of a microwatt and less than 20,000 microwatts. Dotted portions of the threshold curves are extrapolations from the solid portions which represent measurements by Messrs. R. L. Wegel and H. Fletcher of Bell Telephone Laboratories, published in 1922. More recent and accurate thresholds are shown on page 239.

MINIMUM PERCEPTIBLE INCREMENT OF PITCH—The family of curves in Figure 2 shows for each of several

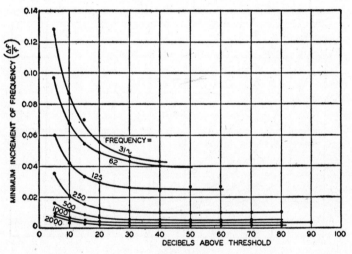

Figure 2

frequencies the minimum increment in frequency which can be detected by the normal ear. For example, the curve labeled 125 gives the minimum interval by which this frequency must be increased or decreased to be just perceptibly different. The interval depends upon the intensity of the original tone. The intensity is plotted along the horizontal axis in decibels above the intensity of a just audible tone of the particular frequency. Corresponding to 20 on that axis, curve 125 has a value of 0.03. This means that a pure tone of 125 + 0.03 × 125 = 128.75, or approximately 129, cycles per second is just distinguishable from one of 125 cycles (B.S.T.M. B-621).

MINIMUM PERCEPTIBLE INCREMENT OF INTENSITY—The curves of Figure 3 show for each of several fre-

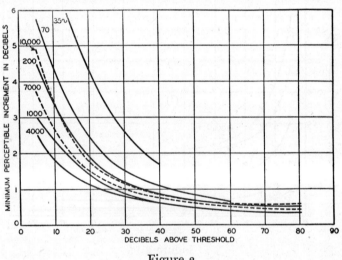

Figure 3

quencies how many decibels the intensity of a tone must be increased in order that its loudness shall be just perceptibly different from that of the original tone. Curve marked "200", for example, indicates for that frequency, by the reading of the vertical scale, "the minimum perceptible increment" of intensity corresponding to any intensity represented on the horizontal scale. If a 200-cycle pure tone is at a level of 20 db above the threshold of audibility it is just distinguishable in loudness from a similar tone which differs in level by 1.9 db. At 40 db the perceptible increment is 0.85 db and at 70 db only 0.5 db. A difference in level of 1.9 db corresponds to a power ratio of 1.55; of 0.85 db to 1.22; and of 0.5 db to 1.12. This means that for 200 cycles the ear cannot distinguish a difference in intensity less than twelve percent and if the tones are relatively weak the difference must be sixty percent or more. For 4000 cycles the ear can discriminate most keenly as indicated by the position of the curve for that frequency. (B.S.T.M. B-325.)

TRANSMISSION CHARACTERISTICS—At the present time the frequency band which is transmitted over the long-distance "program circuits", connecting studios and radio stations, extends from 100 to 5000 cycles. It is possible to transmit a wider band although there are economic considerations because the cost of circuits will increase as the band is widened. What can be accomplished in transmission is indicated by the curves of Figures 4, 5, and 6. In each case the horizontal line (axis of abscissas) is divided on a logarithmic scale as shown. Ordinates for each curve give the ratio of output current to input current expressed in decibels. Figure 4 is for an open-wire circuit between Chicago and San Francisco; Figure 5 is for an experimental cable circuit 2200 miles long looped back and forth over a cable route in the eastern part of the United States; and Figure 6 shows the special circuits used in

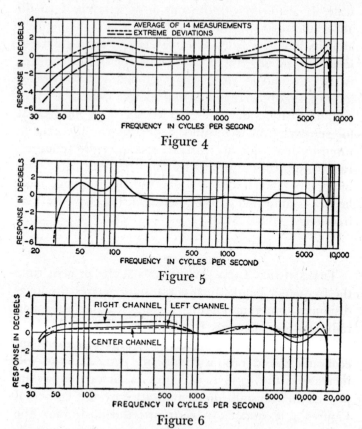

Figure 4

Figure 5

Figure 6

1933 for the transmission of orchestral music from Philadelphia to Washington, c.f. page 74. (B.S.T.M. B-484 and B-784, and Bell Laboratories Record Vol. XIII, No. 6.)

MICROPHONES AND LOUDSPEAKERS—Figure 7 shows the response to pure tones of various frequencies on the part of the moving-coil microphones which were used in the demonstration of auditory perspective described on page 75. The scale of abscissas is logarithmic and shows frequency. The scale of ordinates is in decibels below an arbitrary reference intensity. The microphone response is dependent upon the angle of incidence of the sound upon the diaphragm.

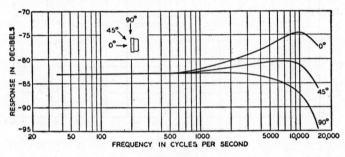

Figure 7

Microphones and loudspeakers, as the conjugate terminal apparatus of a transmission system, should ordinarily be considered together since it is their combined and "overall" performance which determines the faithfulness with which music can be picked up and reproduced. Unfortunately, at least so far as affects simplicity of presentation, the measured output of a loudspeaker is dependent upon the acoustic conditions of the room in which it is placed. (This fact is illustrated by the curves of page 258.) In the case of the Philadelphia-Washington transmission what was of interest to the engineers responsible for the equipment

was the overall effect of microphone and loudspeakers.
This was determined by measuring the acoustic output
of the loudspeaker, or more strictly the musical sound
which it occasioned at some definite point in the auditorium, for an input of sound to the microphone which
was constant in power but progressively varied in frequency. The net result of such an overall test is shown
in Figure 8.

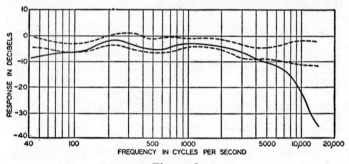

Figure 8

The full line curve of this figure is the output-fre-
quency characteristic of the combination of microphone
and loudspeaker as measured for a point in Constitution
Hall about the middle of the auditorium. The sounds
presented to the distant microphone had approximately
90 degrees incidence.

Equalizing networks were then introduced into the
transmission circuit so as to correct for the net inade-
quacy of the microphone-loudspeaker combination. The
microphones, during the concert, were so located with
reference to the orchestra in the Academy of Music that
they operated practically on the characteristic shown in
Figure 7 for 45 degrees incidence.

The dashed lines in Figure 8 show the final result with equalizers in the circuit. The spread between these lines represents variations corresponding to various possible positions of listeners in the middle of the hall. In the rear of the hall the high frequency tones cannot be heard as well as shown by the dashed lines. Tones of 10,000 cycles, for example, may be down 15 or 20 db as compared to their intensity in the middle of the hall. This loss is due to the absorption of high frequency vibrations in the air. On the other hand, for a listener near the stage tones of very high pitch may be up about as much.

These curves and numerical values illustrate not only what an electrical system can do in the pick-up and reproduction of music but also the wide differences which normally exist in music as heard in different parts of an auditorium. The character and overtone structure of music depends upon where the listener sits. Even for adjacent seats, because of interference patterns (see page 258), the music is not the same.

QUALITY CONTROL NETWORK—Figure 9 shows the characteristics of an additional network which was inserted in the circuit to enhance certain components in the current or to minimize their effects. This network was under the control of the musical director and permitted the variations discussed on page 184.

REVISED THRESHOLDS—Figure 10 shows the latest and most exact determinations of the thresholds of feeling (upper curve) and of hearing (lower curve). For comparison with the scale of frequency there is shown in

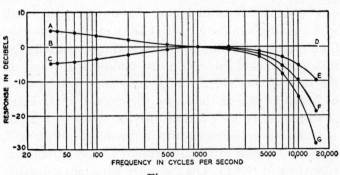

Figure 9

musical notation the corresponding notes. The vertical
scale gives intensity in decibels above the reference level
(discussed on page 85) of 10^{-16} watt. The dotted area
shows the intensities and frequencies of the component
vibrations imposed upon the ear by conversational
speech.

The horizontal scale is logarithmic and so the linear
distance corresponding to a definite musical interval is
constant. For example, the separation of frequencies
100 and 50 is the same as for 400 and 200 or for any
other octave.

The frequency ranges involved in speech and in certain typical noises are indicated by the dot and dash
lines. The dashes extend through the portion of the
frequency range which is found by tests to be essential
to reproduction of the particular sound. That a lesser
range is being reproduced can be detected only eighty
percent of the time (cf. page 130). The dots indicate an
extension of the range for which the percent of correct
judgments is only 60 percent. (Reproduced from Bell
Laboratories Record, 1934.)

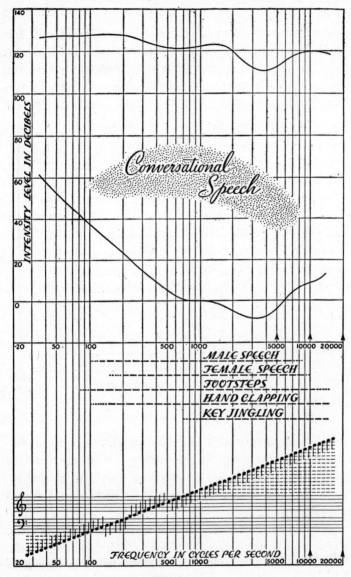

Figure 10
239

LOUDNESS OF PURE TONES—For a tone of any frequency, represented on the horizontal axis of Figure 11,
and for any intensity of that tone, represented on the
vertical axis, there is a loudness which is given by this
family of curves—the loudness level contours. For ex-

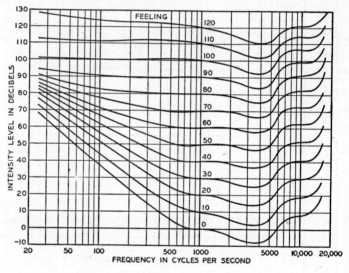

Figure 11

ample, for a tone of 200 cycles 40 db above the reference level the point corresponding lies on the contour
marked 20. That is the loudness level. It is the intensity level of a 1000-cycle tone which would sound
equally loud.

Figure 12 is an alternative arrangement of these data.
Read the intensity of the tone on the horizontal axis.
Find where the vertical erected at that point intersects
the particular curve of the family that corresponds to

the frequency. Then on the vertical scale read the ordi-
nate of the point of intersection to find the loudness.

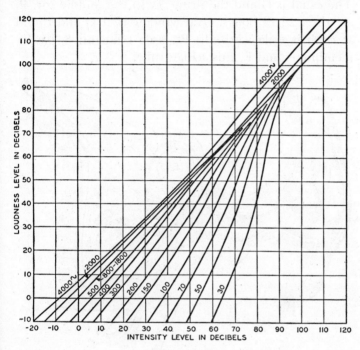

Figure 12

For example, for intensity of 40 and frequency of 200,
the loudness is 21. This compares with 20 as found from
Figure 11 and is within the precision of these plots
and the original experiments. (B.S.T.M. B-756.)

THE EAR—Figure 13, reproduced by permission from
Fletcher's "Speech and Hearing" (D. Van Nostrand
Co., Inc., New York), is a semi-diagrammatic section
through a right ear. The cross-section of the outer and

inner ear are cut by different planes so that the spatial relationship is not exactly that of the plane of the paper. The canal is G and the drum T. In the middle ear, P, are three small bones. Oval window is at O and round at r. Vt is scala vestibuli; Pt, scala tympani; S, basilar membrane; and E, Eustachian tube.

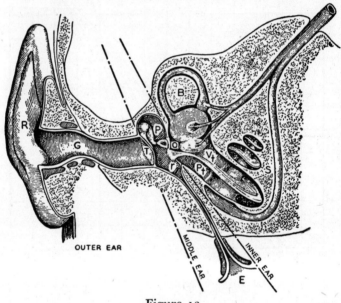

Figure 13

Figure 14, from the same source, shows a cross-section of the cochlea. Figure 15 is a schematic showing how the cochlea would look if straightened out. Figure 16 is a schematic of the cochlea, between the oval window where the stapes applies pressure and the helicotrema, scaled to indicate the regions of the basilar membrane which are affected by various frequencies of vibration.

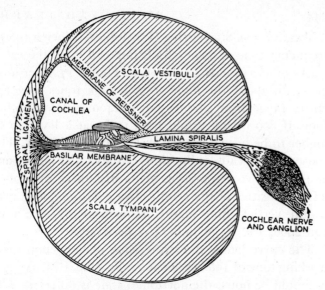

Figure 14

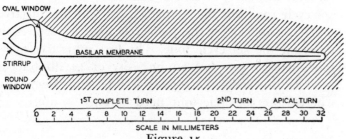

Figure 15

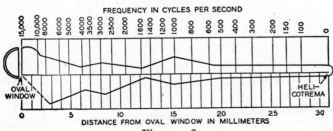

Figure 16

243

MASKING AND SUBJECTIVE HARMONICS—When a single-frequency tone of 500 cycles is imposed upon the ear it masks others sounds, as shown in Figure 17. At a level of 65 db above threshold it will mask tones over the entire range from about 300 to 2400 cycles. Another tone, if 800 cycles, would have to be at a level 40 or higher to be heard; if 1800 cycles, at 10 or higher. The 500-cycle tone causes vibrations of the basilar membrane at positions corresponding to its first three overtones. The intensities of these subjective overtones, as shown by the vertical lines at the frequencies of 1000, 1500 and 2000, are 52, 36, and 14 respectively.

The curve below shows the same phenomenon for a masking tone of 1000 cycles at 72 db. (B.S.T.M. B-499.) It should be noted the horizontal scale is different. The form of the curve is almost identical with that for a 500-cycle tone but the frequencies at which subjective overtones appear for the 1000-cycle tone are octaves of those for the 500-cycle tone. The first subjective overtone in each case has an intensity of 52 db but to produce this effect the 1000-cycle tone must be 72 db, whereas the 500-cycle tone need be only 65 db.

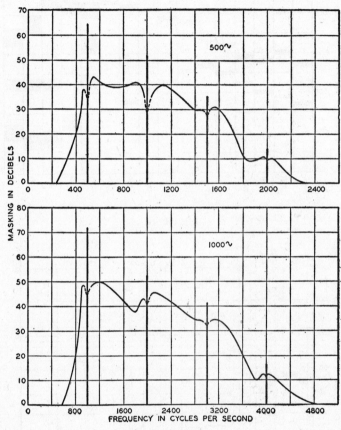

Figure 17

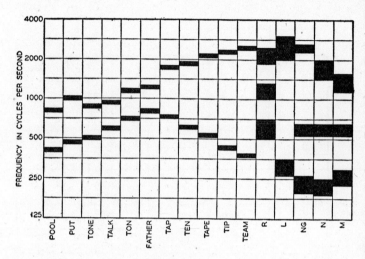

Figure 18

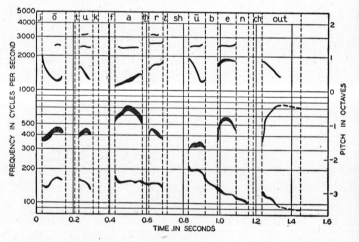

Figure 19

Vowels—Figure 18 (from B.S.T.M. B-568) shows the important characteristic frequencies of the vowel sounds indicated along the horizontal axis. The vertical axis gives the frequency in cycles per second.

Figure 19 (B.S.T.M. B-820) shows with more detail the pitch ranges and variations for the sentence "Joe took father's shoe bench out". This sentence and its associate in telephonic researches, "She was waiting on my lawn" contain the principal spoken sounds of English. Figure 19 was derived by careful harmonic analysis of an oscillogram of the spoken sentence. The sentence was spoken in 1.45 seconds as shown by the horizontal scale. The frequencies of the components in the sound at each instant are plotted with reference to the vertical scale of frequencies. The relative intensities of the several components are approximately indicated by the thickness of the lines, and the melodic changes in frequency by their slopes.

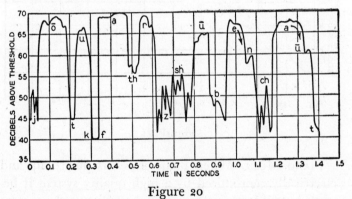

Figure 20

Figure 20 shows for the same sentence the relative intensities of the syllabic sounds.

Figure 21 shows on the left for a man's voice and on the right for a woman's voice the relative maximum intensities of sung vowels of various pitches. See page 127 and its footnote credit reference. The pitch of $C_2\sharp$ at which a man's voice has an acoustic power of about 100 microwatts corresponds to a frequency of 139 cycles per second. Two octaves higher, when his output is one whole watt, the frequency is 554 cycles. From the data plotted in Figures 11 and 12, and upon the reasonably valid assumption that his notes are pure tones, the corresponding loudness levels can be obtained. It will then be evident that his song is not 40 db louder at the higher pitch but appreciably less than that.

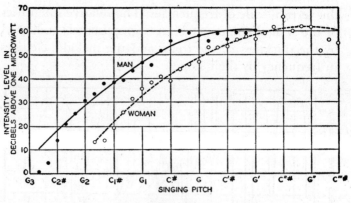

Figure 21

PIANO MUSIC—When piano music is picked up and electrically reproduced by a high quality system it becomes possible through the method discussed on page 130 to determine what range of frequencies is important. Filters are introduced and comparison made with the unfiltered reproduction. The observations are treated statistically; and any difference which a filter may occasion but which cannot be perceived as existing is aurally unimportant.

The curve of Figure 22 shows the percentage of judgments which were correct as to the existence of a distortion due to filtering. "Fifty percent correct" means merely the ordinary correctness which would occur in guessing on the flip of a coin. It means no aural evidence. On that basis, frequencies below 55 cycles and

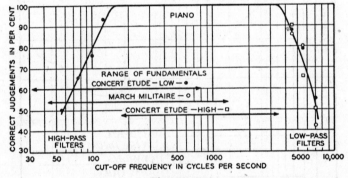

Figure 22

above 7000 are not essential in reproduction. For practical conditions it has been assumed that components, the presence or absence of which cannot be correctly judged more than eighty percent of the time by keeneared listeners under good acoustic conditions, are not essential to high-quality reproduction. On that basis, as the curve shows, the range for the piano extends from 100 to 5000 cycles. The fundamentals of its lower notes are not perceived except subjectively, as discussed on page 112. (B.S.T.M. B-591.)

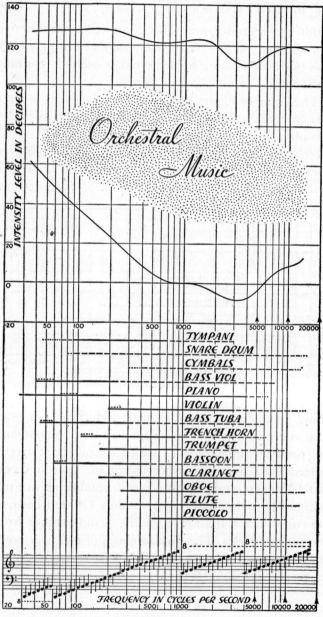

Figure 23
250

FREQUENCY RANGE OF ORCHESTRAL MUSIC—Figure 23, which is similar to Figure 10, shows frequency ranges of the usual orchestral instruments. The experimental procedure was similar to that of page 130. Solid lines show range of fundamentals. Dash lines indicate frequencies correctly judged, as present or absent, eighty percent of the time; and dotted lines those sixty percent of the time. (From chart in Bell Laboratories Record, 1934.)

ORCHESTRAL MUSIC—In Figure 24 the solid portions of the border lines represent the thresholds of hearing

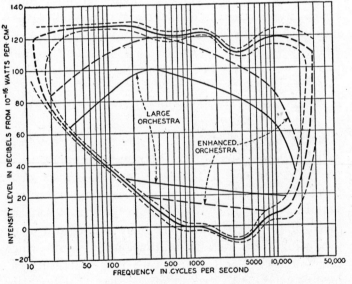

Figure 24

and feeling according to the latest measurements. The thresholds are extrapolated by dashed lines beyond the frequency range, 35-15,000 cycles, over which definitive measurements have been made. Above and below these curves are dotted lines indicating the usual limits of variation in the thresholds of individuals of normal hearing. The portions of the entire hearing range which are utilized in listening to a large orchestra are bounded by the curves marked "large orchestra". The intensity range of such an orchestra is about 70 db, extending from about 30 db above reference level to about 100 db above, in the band of frequencies of greatest intensity.

So far as the ear is concerned orchestral music might have a wider range of intensities. Without falling seriously below the noise level in an auditorium its pianissimo might be 10 db lower; and without becoming painful its forte might rise 20 db higher. Such a wider range of "enhanced" orchestral music is possible if it is electro-acoustically reproduced. (B.S.T.M. B-784.)

SOUND RECORDING—Figure 25 shows a short length of variable density sound track on film for a pure tone of 100 cycles per second. The equivalent in chemical density of the molecular condensations and rarefactions of a sound wave are clearly visible. This film travels a steady speed of 18 inches per second in recording and in reproducing. The track is for the loudest sound which can be recorded without clashing of the vibrating elements of the light valve. Figure 26 shows the track for an intensity about 8 db lower.

Figure 27 shows a "variable area" oscillographic sound track for the word "Joe". The corresponding frequencies may be obtained from Figure 19.

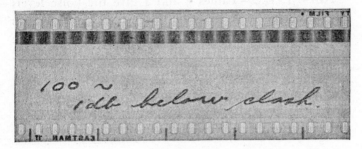

Figure 25

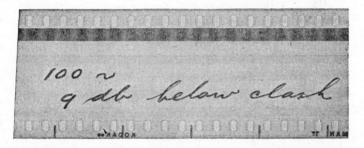

Figure 26

Figure 27

NOISE LEVELS—Tables 3 and 4 give the noise levels
of typical sounds or acoustic conditions for out-of-doors
and for in-doors, respectively. The levels indicated are
compilations of the results of several observers, as indicated by the note in each table.

TABLE 3—OUT-OF-DOOR NOISE LEVELS

Noise Level

130 db	Threshold of painful sound
113	Hammering on steel, two feet away
101–94	Pneumatic riveter, 35 feet away
97–88	Subway station platform
94–92	Loud steamship whistle, 100 feet
102–72	Automobile horns, 20 feet
91–85	Elevated train from 15–20 feet
87–86	Lion or tiger in Zoo, 10–15 feet
87–55	Motor trucks, 15–50 feet
85–48	Busy city streets
68	Approximate average for busy city street
65	Ordinary conversation, 3 feet
68–42	Quiet residential street
45–37	About the minimum for city noises
30–20	Quiet suburban garden in London, as reported by A. H. Davis
10	About the out-of-door minimum
0	Threshold of hearing

(Abstracted from the report of the New York City Noise Abatement
Commission and B.S.T.M. B-506.)

TABLE 4—INDOOR NOISE LEVELS

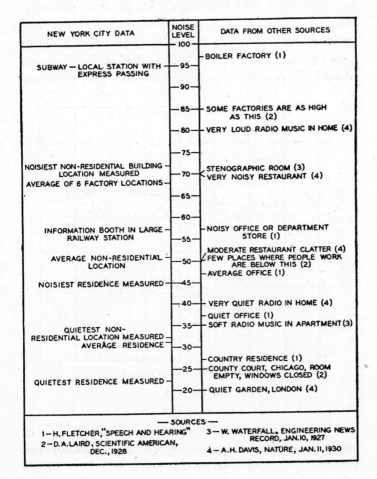

NEW YORK CITY DATA	NOISE LEVEL	DATA FROM OTHER SOURCES
	— 100 —	
	— 95 —	BOILER FACTORY (1)
SUBWAY — LOCAL STATION WITH EXPRESS PASSING		
	— 90 —	
	— 85 —	SOME FACTORIES ARE AS HIGH AS THIS (2)
	— 80 —	VERY LOUD RADIO MUSIC IN HOME (4)
	— 75 —	
NOISIEST NON-RESIDENTIAL BUILDING LOCATION MEASURED	— 70 —	STENOGRAPHIC ROOM (3) VERY NOISY RESTAURANT (4)
AVERAGE OF 6 FACTORY LOCATIONS		
	— 65 —	
	— 60 —	
INFORMATION BOOTH IN LARGE RAILWAY STATION	— 55 —	NOISY OFFICE OR DEPARTMENT STORE (1)
AVERAGE NON-RESIDENTIAL LOCATION	— 50 —	MODERATE RESTAURANT CLATTER (4) FEW PLACES WHERE PEOPLE WORK ARE BELOW THIS (2) AVERAGE OFFICE (1)
NOISIEST RESIDENCE MEASURED	— 45 —	
	— 40 —	VERY QUIET RADIO IN HOME (4)
	— 35 —	QUIET OFFICE (1) SOFT RADIO MUSIC IN APARTMENT (3)
QUIETEST NON-RESIDENTIAL LOCATION MEASURED AVERAGE RESIDENCE	— 30 —	
	— 25 —	COUNTRY RESIDENCE (1) COUNTY COURT, CHICAGO, ROOM EMPTY, WINDOWS CLOSED (2)
QUIETEST RESIDENCE MEASURED	— 20 —	QUIET GARDEN, LONDON (4)

— SOURCES —

1 — H. FLETCHER, "SPEECH AND HEARING"

2 — D. A. LAIRD, SCIENTIFIC AMERICAN, DEC., 1928

3 — W. WATERFALL, ENGINEERING NEWS RECORD, JAN. 10, 1927

4 — A. H. DAVIS, NATURE, JAN. 11, 1930

AUDIOGRAM.—Figure 28 shows the audiograms of four different ears, three of which indicate moderate hearing difficulties and the fourth an extreme difficulty. The horizontal scale is plotted in octaves from 1000 cycles as zero; thus —2 means 250 cycles and 2 means 4000 cycles. The reference level is that of the threshold of audibility; and the vertical scale indicates the num-

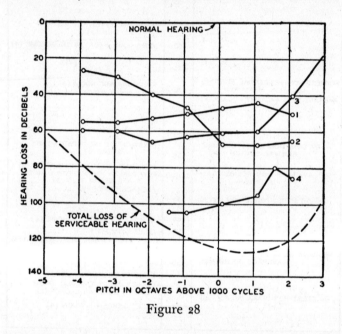

Figure 28

ber of decibels of hearing loss. For example, the ear of audiogram numbered 3 cannot hear any tones between pitches of 62 and 2000 which are not at least 60 db more intense than would be necessary for a normal ear. Notice that this ear hears the higher frequency tones more easily than the low, a condition the opposite of ear numbered 2. Listeners with these ears cannot help forming markedly different judgments of music either instrumental or vocal. Critics of music should know their own audiograms.

REVERBERATION TIME—Reverberation time, as originally defined by W. C. Sabine, is the time required, after a source of sound has ceased to operate, for the sound to drop to one millionth of its intensity, that is through 60 decibel steps. The measurement is made ordinarily for a pure tone of 512 cycles per second. The time for a 1000-cycle tone is slightly less, about 0.95 of that for 512 cycles.

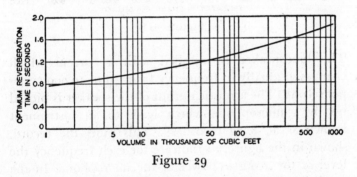

Figure 29

Figure 29 gives an indication of the reverberation times for a 1000-cycle tone which are generally accepted as satisfactory for various sizes of auditorium. There is, however, no narrow range or absolutely optimum value; and reverberation times fifteen or twenty percent higher than those plotted will be acceptable to audiences and to musical experts. The times are for full audiences. (B.S.T.M. B-466.)

REVERBERATION AND MICROPHONE PLACEMENT—Figure 30, which shows the "response" of a loudspeaker under two different conditions, is an excellent illustration of the interference patterns mentioned on page 171.

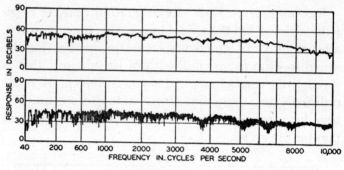

Figure 30

The loudspeaker is supplied with a current which changes gradually in frequency from 40 to 10,000 cycles per second. The acoustic output of the speaker is picked up by a microphone which leads to an instrument known as a "level recorder". This plots the record, shown in the figure, to indicate for each frequency the level of the acoustic power at the microphone. In the condition for the upper curve the microphone is only two feet from the speaker; and, therefore, in the total of sound it picks up, the ratio of direct to reverberant is higher than in the condition for the lower curve where the microphone is eight feet away. For that reason the variations in reverberation between sounds of different frequencies are more obvious in the second situation. So complex are the reflections in an ordinary hall that the pattern differs from point-to-point throughout the hall. A slight change in position of the microphone would have recorded a curve of similar appearance but altogether different set of values. (Bell Laboratories Record, vol. 13, No. 3.)

DIRECTIONAL EFFECTS OF MUSICAL INSTRUMENTS— Figure 31 is the polar plot for the acoustic pressure

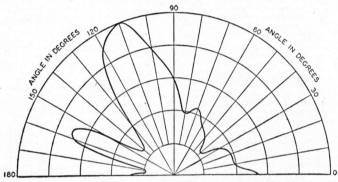

Figure 31

established by a violin, which was described on page 174. Reproduced from an article by Backhaus (Zeit. für Tech. Physik, 1928).

ATMOSPHERIC ABSORPTION OF SOUND—As was stated in Chapter 2 the intensity of a sound decreases as it gets farther and farther from its source. Its intensity at any point is inversely as the square of the distance to that point.

In addition to this reduction which is due to the spreading of the energy over a larger and larger area there is an absorption of some of the acoustic energy in the intervening air. This absorption is not the same for all frequencies; hence there is always some distortion of a sound during its transmission through air—and the amount by which various frequencies are discriminated against increases with the distance. This absorption is different for different conditions of humidity.

Figure 32, which is adapted from data published by V. O. Knudsen in the "Journal of the Acoustical So-

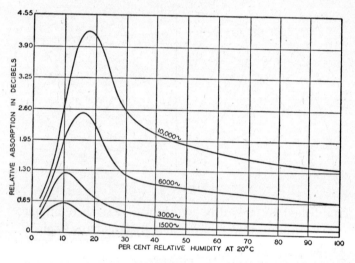

Figure 32

ciety of America," April, 1935, gives the absorption for various frequencies and conditions of humidity for a path in air of 50 feet.

As a numerical illustration consider a sound intensity at a seat of a hall, say 50 feet from a soloist. At a seat 150 feet away, that is 3 times as far away, the sound intensity is one-ninth. It would be down about 9.5 db if there were no absorption. If the humidity is 30 percent and the frequency is 3000 cycles it is down in addition 0.4 db for each fifty feet. Due to both distance and air absorption it is, therefore, down 10.3 db. On the other hand, if the frequency is 6000 cycles the air absorption is 2.4 db and the total difference of level between 50 and 150 feet is 11.9 db.

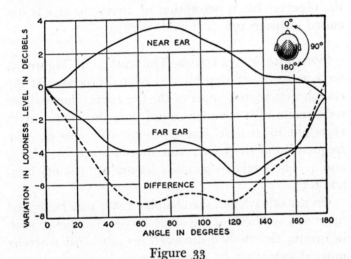

Figure 33

The absorption introduces but little distortion into the direct sound. In the reverberant sound of an auditorium it will introduce much more because of the longer path. A sound may travel one or two thousand feet before it contributes at some point to the reverberant sound. In 1000 feet at 30 percent humidity the 6000-cycle sound will be down 24 db and the 3000-cycle 8 db—a discrimination of 16 db between the two tones.

BINAURAL AUDITION—The full-line curves of Figure 33 show the variations in loudness of speech as its source changes its direction from front to back to a binaural listener. As the source gets opposite one ear the loudness is greater in that ear and less in the other. The dotted curve shows the net difference. On the basis of that, and the difference in the quality of the sound, the observer has a perception of direction, as was discussed on page 178 (B.S.T.M. B-784.)

SYNTHETIC WAVE-FORMS—The curves in Figure 34 serve as an illustration for two related processes. If the complex curve, the upper of the five curves shown, is an oscillogram of a complex sound then the other curves represent its analysis into harmonic components. The frequencies of the component sinusoids are as: 1, 2, 3, and 4. Their relative amplitudes are as: 1, 0.67, 0.37, and 0.37.

On the other hand, the complex curve may be looked upon as a synthesis of the other curves. The figure then illustrates the method discussed on page 191, whereby musical tones may be produced with harmonics in any desired relationship of amplitude. It is obvious that if one of the component curves were displaced to the right, or to the left, the form of the complex curve would be changed. Expressed in more technical terms, the wave-form is dependent upon the phase of the components, that is upon the relative time at which their maxima occur.

It is important to note, however, that what the ear responds to is the component pure tones. Its response is independent of differences in wave-form provided the components remain the same in frequency and relative amplitude. In other words, the ear does not recognize phase differences. These statements are correct provided that the intensity of the sound is not sufficient to overload the ear and if the waves are sustained as would be true of a musical note as distinct from a sharp click.

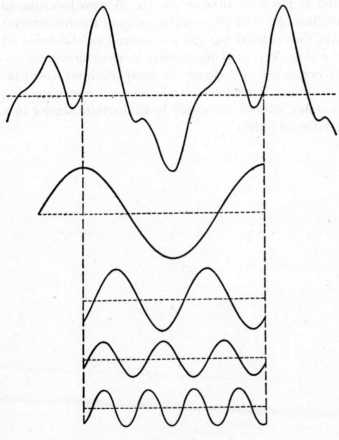

Figure 34

These facts were strikingly demonstrated some years ago in an experiment in the Bell Laboratories which made use of the generators of pure tone mentioned on page 113. The individual generators were set to produce certain pure tones of definite intensities. Arrangements were then made to listen to the resulting complex tone and at the same time to observe its wave-form on an oscilloscope. The phase relationship of the components was then altered but the ear noticed no difference in the tone. Very striking changes in wave-form were unaccompanied by a change in aural sensation. Incidentally, this is another reason why an oscilloscope, showing complex wave-forms, would be of doubtful service to a teacher of music.

INDEX

INDEX

DO YOU KNOW WHY THE BASS NOTE
IN BAND MUSIC
SOUND LOUDER
AS THE BAND
APPROACHES?

THERE ARE TONES IN ORCHESTRAL MUSIC
WHICH COULD BE
OMITTED WITH-
OUT BEING
MISSED.

A LION'S ROAR IS A HUNDRED MILLION
TIMES MORE IN-
TENSE THAN IS
NECESSARY FOR
AUDIBILITY.

DO YOU KNOW WHY SOME RADIO
SINGERS OR SPEAK-
ERS SEEM SO
INTIMATE?